SHORT SEA SHIPPING
1999/2000

by
Gilbert Mayes
and
Bernard McCall

INTRODUCTION

We are delighted to be publishing this third edition of what has now become the definitive guide to short sea cargo vessels owned, managed, chartered or agented by companies in the United Kingdom and Republic of Ireland. Since the publication of the first edition in 1995, the trend to use larger vessels on traditional "short sea" routes has continued. Indeed it is becoming increasingly rare to see a coaster of less than 1000 tonnes deadweight. This applies in the tanker trades just as much as in the dry cargo trades. Obviously these larger ships offer economies of scale so vital in the competitve world of transport. The downside of larger vessels is that small ports which are limited in access are now visited far less frequently.

To enhance the value of this book as work of historical reference in addition to being a an up-to-date handbook, the Index of ship names has been much extended to include all former names of ships. It will thus be a useful cross-reference for vessels listed in previous issues which have since changed name. The book contains over 800 ship names and almost 200 company titles.

As noted in the 1997 edition, ship owning is a complex business and the terminology used in this book reflects this complexity. It is often more useful to speak about the "operator" of a ship than the owner; the latter is often a bank or similar financial institution far removed from the world of shipping. Within the company listings in this book, there are terms such as "managers for" and "agents for". In using these terms, we have followed the wishes of the operators and we have identified their involvement in the ships in the way they have requested. It is worth noting that some companies are included simply because the vessels which they operate fly the flag of the United Kingdom, one of its dependencies, the Isle of Man, or the Republic of Ireland.

Once again, we are grateful to all the operators for their willing assistance, encouragement and practical comments when answering the many queries which we put to them in order to ensure accuracy and up-to-date information. Without their help and support, the book in this format would not be possible. We have tried to check all details thoroughly but we cannot accept any reponsibility for errors or omissions, or their consequences. We hope that readers will let us know of any such problems. Ship details are corrected to 31 December 1998 and all technical details are the latest available at the time of going to press.

The following information is given for each ship:

	Col 1	Col 2	Col 3	Col 4	Col 5	Col 6	Col 7	Col 8
SHIP NAME (Flag)	Year	Gross	Deadwt	Length	Breadth	Draught	Service	Ship
(previous names and	Built	Tonnage	Tonnage	(LOA)	Extreme	Loaded	Speed	Type
year of change)								

Flag abbreviations comply with ISO 3166/1988

We owe a debt of gratitude to many. The staff and publications of *Lloyd's Register of Shipping* have, as always, been invaluable. Many individuals, too numerous to mention, have answered a succession of queries. Thanks must go to all the photographers whose work has been used and to those who submitted photographs which we were not able to use. With such a collection of data, considerable cross-checking is needed especially with the Index; thanks to Annie and John Southwood for their assistance in this respect. The staff of Dalton Printers have provided excellent service. Last but certainly not least, we wish to record our thanks to our respective families who show limitless (almost!) patience and provide help and support at (almost!) all times.

Gil Mayes   Bernard McCall
(*Launcherley*)   (*Portishead*)

March 1999

ACOMARIT (U.K.) LTD.

The Skypark, 8 Elliot Place, Glasgow, G3 8EP
(0141 243-2435/fax 0141 243-2436. E-mail: contact @ acomarit.com)
Managers for:

Mimosa Marine Shipping Co

BAUSKA	*(CYP)*	87	14937	23050	158,3	26,0	10,0	15	tk

(Launched as Nord Skagerrak)

Roroki Ltd

NORCLIFF	*(NIS)*	95	8407	5866	125,3	19,7	7,0	14	ro/pt

(Launched as Crown Link)

Crusader Shipholding Ltd

THALIA	*(PAN)*	85	4711	7569	115,0	17,8	6,9	13	oil/ch tk

(ex Cape Spirit-96, Stainless Mariner-95, Shoun Venture-89)

ACOMARIT (U.K.) LTD.

28 Rutland Square, Edinburgh, EH1 2BW (0131 221 9441/fax 0131 221 9313)
Technical Managers for:

Liquid Gas Shipping Ltd

TARQUIN FORTH	*(PAN)*	98	6160	7950					lpg
TARQUIN GLEN	*(LBR)*	91	2985	3590	88,4	14,2	5,1	15	lpg
TARQUIN GROVE	*(LBR)*	92	2985	3590	88,4	14,2	6,2	15	lpg
TARQUIN MARINER	*(LBR)*	92	3693	4444	99,4	15,0	6,4	15	lpg
TARQUIN PRIDE	*(PAN)*	98	6051	7590					lpg
TARQUIN ROVER	*(LBR)*	94	5821	5704	115,3	16,8	5,1	15	lpg

(Launched as Val Metavro)

Liquid Gas (Isle of Man) Ltd

TARQUIN BRAE	*(LBR)*	97	5420	7246	113,5	16,5	7,6	15	lpg
TARQUIN MOOR	*(LBR)*	97	5420	7246	113,5	16,5	7,6	15	lpg

Tarquinius Compagnia di Navigazione

TARQUIN NAVIGATOR	*(LBR)*	95	5821	5632	115,3	16,8	7,0	15	lpg

Pentland Gas Carriers Ltd

TARQUIN RANGER	*(LBR)*	94	4317	5771	105,4	15,7	7,0	15	lpg

Tarquin Shipping Co S.A.

TARQUIN TRADER	*(LBR)*	88	3595	4320	98,3	15,0	6,6	15	lpg

*The **TARQUIN TRADER** at anchor in Swansea Bay on 21 June 1998.* (Danny Lynch)

ADOHR ISLAND TRADING LTD.

Kilronan, Inish Mor, Aran Islands, Co. Galway, Irish Republic

INISHLYRE *(HND)*	65	199	249	33,3	7,3	2,7	9	gen

(ex Newfyne-97, Glenfyne-88)

ALBA SHIPPING LTD A/S.

Gasvaerskvej 48, PO Box 636, 9100 Aalborg, Denmark, (+45 98 16 30 33/fax +45 98 16 16 33)

KASLA *(IOM)*	74	4724	6863	130,3	17,6	6,3	14	tk

(ex Kiisla-96)

Managers for:

K/S Jurong

BUNA *(IOM)*	79	1561	1802	73,4	12,3	4,9	13	bk tk

Lauter Shipping Ltd

SITULA *(IOM)*	65	1049	2000	69,8	10,4	3,8	11	tk

(ex Neptun-68)

ALDERNEY SHIPPING CO LTD.

White Rock, St Peter Port, Guernsey, CI, GY1 2LN (01481 724810/fax 01481 724810. E-mail: allied .coasters @ virgin.net) and 11 Victoria Street, Alderney, via Guernsey, CI (01481 822828/fax 01481 822065)

Managers for:

Felix Shipping Ltd

ISIS *(IOM)*	78	674	953	57,5	10,1	3,4	11	gen(25c)

(ex Deer Sound-94, David Dorman-89)

Unicorn Ltd

BURHOU I *(GBR)*	78	674	953	57,5	10.1	3,4	11	gen

(ex Lancresse-97, Bressay Sound-94, Edgar Dorman-89)

Ortac Ltd

ORTAC *(VCT)*	74	891	1400	60,9	9,8	4,3	11	gen

(ex Teal I-97, Hoxa Sound-94, Murell-88)

*Alderney Shipping's **BURHOU I** approaches St Peter Port, Guernsey, on 8 May 1998.* (Peter Stewart)

ALEXANDERS PARTNERS (SHIPBROKING) LTD

267 Cranbrook Road, Ilford, Essex, IG1 4TG (0181 518 3190/fax 0181 518 3009)

Chartering Managers/Agents for:

Stephenson Clarke Shipping Ltd, demise chartered to **Point Shipping Co**, Dundalk

DUNANY	*(IRL)*	83	1785	2535	77,1	13,2	5,0	12	gen

(ex Cowdray-94, Ballygrainey-90)

Mideast Marine Ltd & Fern Trading Ltd

EASTFERN	*(IRL)*	81	1171	1644	70,6	10,8	4,3	10	gen

(ex Arklow Abbey-96)

Hope Shipping Corp

HOPE	*(BRB)*	82	1785	2535	77,1	13,2	5,0	12	gen

(ex Shoreham-93, Ballygarvey-90)

Roca Shipping Corp

KISH	*(BRB)*	78	1961	2973	84,2	13,9	5,4	14	gen

(ex Niewiadow-93, launched as Ran)

Aniara Shipping Co Ltd

ROMEO	*(CYP)*	83	1908	3152	81,6	14,1	5,4	11	gen

(ex Andromeda-93)

Note : Alexanders Partners *are also chartering managers/agents for vessels listed under other owners*

Having loaded her cargo, the **KISH** heads out to sea from Llysfaen Jetty, Llanddulas, on 24 May 1996.

(John P Evans)

ALLANTONE SUPPLIES LTD.

139 Hamilton Road, Felixstowe, Suffolk, IP11 7BL (01394 670001/fax 01394 671202)

Managers for:

Southern Bunkering Ltd

CONOCOAST	*(GBR)*	68	209	330	35,3	7,6	2,7	8	tk

(ex Surehand-94, Bouncer-89)

General Port Services Ltd

CONTRACTOR	*(GBR)*	61	135	240	39,6	5,1	2,3	8	tk bge

(ex Conostream-96, Torfen, Blackmartin C)

CONVEYOR	*(GBR)*	80	198	307	33,5	6,6	2,4	7	tk
DELSTOR	*(GBR)*	57	155	260	42,0	5,3	2,1	7	tk bge
ONWARD MARINER	*(GBR)*	70	239	339	40,2	6,7	2,5	8	tk

Note. *The company is associated with* General Port Services Ltd.

The **ONWARD MARINER** was photographed at Southampton on 6 February 1997. *(Chris Bancroft)*

AMBRA SHIPMANAGEMENT LTD.
P.O. Box 6668, 3309 Limassol, Cyprus (+5 350469/ fax +5 352937)
Managers for:
Westermoor Shipping Co Ltd
ZIM ESPANA *(GBR)*   77   3807   4150   97,5   16,0   5,7   14   gen(284c)
   (ex West Moor-95, Westermoor-86, Essex Courage-83, Westermoor-83)

ANEKTA MARINE LTD.
Gate 14, Gallions Point Marina, Woolwich Manor Way, London, E16 2PU
(0171 511 7751/fax 0171 511 7750)
LENNARD *(GBR)*   1886   150   200   36,2   4,9   2,0   11   bk tk bge
   (ex Mercurius-90, Hofik, Trude, Koopvaart 16, Koopvaart 7)

ANGLO DUTCH MANAGEMENT SERVICES LTD.
PO Box 1, Woking, Surrey, GU22 0YL (01483 757563/fax 01483 757593)
Managers for:
Labrador Shipping Ltd
ELM *(VCT)*   75   959   1450   65,0   10,8   4,1   12   gen
   (ex Wilhelmina V-97)
Conroy (Cyprus) Ltd
IVY *(CYP)*   75   1483   2320   76,4   12,0   4,8   10   gen
   (ex Daniel D-98, Daniella-94, Daniel-87)
Foreshore Management Ltd
OAK *(BRB)*   72   1327   2230   76,5   12,1   4,6   11   gen
   (ex Lady Sandra-97, Hendrik B-95, Ventura-94)

ARAM RESOURCES Plc.
Mabe,Penryn, Cornwall (01326 375660)
ARENA   60   530   721   52,5   8,8   3,9   10   sand
   (ex Underas Sandtag VI-95, Carina-69, Norsklint-65)

ARC MARINE LTD.
Burnley Wharf, Marine Parade, Southampton,SO14 5JF (01703 828200/ fax 01703 828248)
ARCO ADUR *(GBR)*   88   3498   5360   98,3   17,7   6,3   12   sd
ARCO DART *(GBR)*   90   1309   1700   68,1   13,0   4,1   10   sd
ARCO DEE *(GBR)*   90   1309   1812   67,7   13,0   4,1   10   sd

Name		Year	GT	DWT	Length	Breadth	Draft	Speed	Type
ARCO HUMBER	(GBR)	72	5487	8962	107,0	20,1	7,4	14	sd
(ex Deepstone-86)									
ARCO TRENT	(GBR) *	71	814	835	63,6	9,9	3,3	10	sd
(ex Amey I-74) ·									

Managers/operators of:
Lombard Lessors Ltd

Name		Year	GT	DWT	Length	Breadth	Draft	Speed	Type
ARCO ARUN	(GBR)	87	3476	5360	98,3	17,5	6,3	12	sd

BMI (No.3) Ltd

Name		Year	GT	DWT	Length	Breadth	Draft	Speed	Type
ARCO AVON	(GBR)	86	3474	5360	98,3	17,5	6,3	12	sd

MCC Leasing (No.21) Ltd

Name		Year	GT	DWT	Length	Breadth	Draft	Speed	Type
ARCO AXE	(GBR)	89	3498	5348	98,3	17,7	6,3	12	sd

Civil & Marine Ltd

Name		Year	GT	DWT	Length	Breadth	Draft	Speed	Type
ARCO BECK	(GBR)	89	3325	4745	99,6	17,0	6,3	12	sd
(ex Cambeck-97)									
ARCO BOURNE	(GBR)	81	3249	4557	97,5	17,1	6,3	12	sd
(ex Cambourne-97)									
CAMBRAE	(GBR) *	73	4107	5202	99,8	17,1	7,3	12	sd

Hambros Leasing Ltd

Name		Year	GT	DWT	Length	Breadth	Draft	Speed	Type
ARCO DIJK	(BHS)	92	4960	9823	113,2	19,6	7,7	12	sd
(ex Camdijk-97)									

Consolidated Gold Fields PLC

Name		Year	GT	DWT	Length	Breadth	Draft	Speed	Type
ARCO SEVERN	(GBR)	74	1915	2806	81,5	14,1	5,0	12	sd
ARCO THAMES	(GBR)	74	2929	4357	98,5	15,5	5,4	12	sd
ARCO TYNE	(GBR)	75	2973	4357	98,5	15,5	5,4	13	sd

Note : * currently laid up

ARGOMANN FERRY SERVICE
(Argo Reederei/Mann & Son (London) Ltd), Naval House, Kings Quay Street, Harwich, Essex,
CO12 3JJ (01255 245200/fax 01255 245219)
Chartered tonnage:
Rederi AB Engship

Name		Year	GT	DWT	Length	Breadth	Draft	Speed	Type
GARDEN	(FIN)	77	10762	7200	150,9	19,3	7,0	18	ro(115u)
(ex Liro Sun-93, Bore Sun-92)									

New building (Aker Finnyards, Rauma Yd No. 423)

Name		Year	GT	DWT	Length	Breadth	Draft	Speed	Type
ESTRADEN	(FIN) *	99		9300	162,7	25,2	6,6	19	ro(140u)

Note : * Launched under this name but likely to be renamed in conseqence of charter.

ARKLOW SHIPPING LTD.
North Quay, Arklow, Co.Wicklow, Irish Republic
(+353 402 39901/fax +353 402 39902. E-mail: chartering @ asl.ie)

Name		Year	GT	DWT	Length	Breadth	Draft	Speed	Type
ARKLOW SPIRIT	(IRL)	95	2271	3211	89,9	12,6	4,7	11	gen(116c)
ARKLOW SPRAY	(IRL)	96	2300	3193	89,9	12,6	4,7	11	gen(116c)

Managers for:
Arklow Shipping (Overseas) Ltd

Name		Year	GT	DWT	Length	Breadth	Draft	Speed	Type
ARKLOW BAY	(IRL)	88	1524	2181	73,9	11,8	4,4	10	gen(73c)
ARKLOW MANOR	(IRL)	87	1524	2181	73,9	11,8	4,4	10	gen(73c)
ARKLOW MARSH	(IRL)	88	1524	2183	73,9	11,8	4,4	10	gen(73c)
ARKLOW MILL	(IRL)	88	1524	2179	73,9	11,8	4,4	10	gen(73c)
ARKLOW MOOR	(IRL)	90	1524	2172	73,9	11,8	4,4	10	gen(73c)

Devon Line Ltd

Name		Year	GT	DWT	Length	Breadth	Draft	Speed	Type
ARKLOW BRIDGE	(IRL)	96	4783	7182	99,9	17,2	6,8	12	gen
ARKLOW BROOK	(IRL)	95	4783	7182	99,9	17,2	6,8	12	gen

Arklow Containers Ltd

Name		Year	GT	DWT	Length	Breadth	Draft	Speed	Type
ARKLOW CASTLE	(IRL)	96	5006	6807	116,4	19,4	7,1	17	gen(549c)

Coastal Partnership 1997 Ltd

ARKLOW FAITH *(IRL)* (ex MB Thames-97)	92	2373	4245	88,3	13,2	5,5	11	gen(128c)

Rossquay Ltd

ARKLOW FAME *(IRL)* (ex MB Avon-97)	92	2373	4245	88,3	13,2	5,5	11	gen(128c)

Amoy Enterprises Ltd

ARKLOW FORTUNE *(IRL)* (ex MB Humber-97)	92	2373	4245	88,3	13,2	5,5	11	gen(128c)
ARKLOW FREEDOM *(IRL)* (ex MB Clyde-97)	92	2373	4245	88,3	13,2	5,5	11	gen(128c)

Sailaway Sailor Ltd

ARKLOW MEADOW *(IRL)*	90	1524	2172	73,9	11,8	4,4	10	gen(73c)

Rederij Sonnega B.V.

ARKLOW SAND *(NLD)*	98	2316	3193	89,9	12,5	4,7	11	gen(116c)

Rederij Makkinga B.V.

ARKLOW SEA *(NLD)*	98	2316	3193	89,9	12,6	4,7	11	gen(116c)

On 25 October 1998, the **ARKLOW SEA** became the first Dutch registered Arklow vessel to enter her "home" port of Arklow. She also set a new record by loading the largest cargo ever handled at the port - 3000 tons of fertiliser.

(Pat Davis)

Invermore Shipping Ltd

ARKLOW VALE *(IRL)*	89	2867	4289	88,2	13,7	5,8	11	gen(173c)
ARKLOW VALLEY *(IRL)*	92	2827	4299	88,2	13,7	5,8	11	gen(173c)
ARKLOW VENTURE *(IRL)*	90	2827	4299	88,2	13,7	5,8	11	gen(173c)
ARKLOW VIEW *(IRL)*	91	2827	4299	88,2	13,7	5,8	11	gen(173c)
ARKLOW VIKING *(IRL)*	90	2827	4299	88,2	13,7	5,8	11	gen(173c)
ARKLOW VILLA *(IRL)*	91	2827	4299	88,2	13,7	5,8	11	gen(173c)

Coastal Shipping Ltd

ARKLOW VALOUR *(IRL)*	90	2827	4299	88,2	13,7	5,8	11	gen(173c)
DUNKERQUE EXPRESS *(IRL)*	85	1839	2230	78,6	12,7	4,3	11	gen(124c)

(ex Inisheer-95, Lia Ventura-88, Flagship I-86, Elisa von Barssel-85)

INISHFREE *(IRL)* (ex Lenneborg-97)	83	3222	5327	82,4	15,8	7,5	11	gen(164c)

Penny Hope Co Ltd

GARIBALDI *(CYP)* (ex Shevrell-98)	81	1895	3033	83,8	12,6	5,2	10	gen

AVIATION & FREIGHT SERVICES

The Hill, Main Street (Upper), Clogherhead, Drogheda, Co Louth, Irish Republic
(+ 353 41 9822081/fax + 353 41 9881147
Chartered tonnage:

Navios Puerto de Esmira S.A.

ROYAL 1 *(BLZ)*   58   465   692   52,8   8,8   3,2   9   gen
(ex Boy 1-98, Boye 1-96, Marta Boye-96, Dorthe Boye-88, Marie Boye-86, Klintberg-78)

BANKS SEAFARMS LTD

Coel-na-Mara, St Margaret's Hope, Orkney, KW17 2TL (01856 831226)

LYRAWA BAY *(GBR)*   70   101   45   27,1   7,5   3,0   9   ro(2u)
(ex Sam-76)

BELFAST FREIGHT FERRIES LTD. (BFF)

Victoria Terminal 1, Dargan Road, Belfast, BT3 9LJ (01232 770112/fax 01232 781217)

SPHEROID *(IOM)*   71   7171   2838   124,2   19,2   5,0   19   ro(62u)
(ex Niekerk-87, RoRo Trader-85, Starmark-81)

Operators of:

Lombard Corporate Finance

RIVER LUNE *(BHS)*   83   7765   5000   121,5   21,0   5,3   15   ro(80u)
(ex Stena Topper-93, Salar-93, Stena Topper-89, Bazias 7-89, Balder Vik-86)

Capital Leasing Ltd

SAGA MOON *(GIB)*   84   7746   2900   124,4   17,5   5,2   17   ro(62u)
(ex Lidartindur-86)

Note: Vessels are managed by CELTIC MARINE *qv.*

Chartered tonnage:

Rosal S.A.

DART 4 *(BHS)*   85   9088   4734   120,0   21,0   5,3   14   ro(80u)
(ex Sally Eurolink-97, Bazias 4-93, Balder Bre-85)

MERLE *(BHS)*   84   9088   4734   120,0   21,0   5,3   15   ro(80u)
(ex Sally Euroroute-96, Bazias 3-93, Balder Sten-85)

Note: The company is a wholly owned subsidiary of Cenargo Ltd. *See also* MERCHANT FERRIES *and* V SHIPS.

*The ro-ro ferry **MERLE** has worked on several short sea routes. She was photographed on 26 November 1996 as she left Belfast via the Herdman Channel.*   *(Alan Geddes)*

ALAN C. BENNETT & SONS LTD.

Lingley House, Commissioners Road, Strood, Rochester, Kent, ME2 4EE
(01634 290780/fax 01634 290891)

TRACY BENNETT *(GBR)*	63	730	1210	55,5	11,3	4,4	9	sand
(ex David Marley-91)									

B G FREIGHT LINE LTD

Coastal Terminal, Alexandra Road Extension, Dublin 1, Irish Republic
(+00 353 1 8364342/fax +00 353 1 8364734)
Chartered tonnage:

ATLANTIK *(ATG)*	93	4193	5575	111,1	16,2	6,6	16	gen(417c)
(ex Birgit Jurgens-98)								
Hermann Suhr Schiffahrts KG								
CUXHAVEN *(ATG)*	76	2245	2560	81,4	13,4	5,0	13	gen(162c)
Partenreederei m.s. "Francop" Gerd Bartels KG								
FRANCOP *(ATG)*	91	3818	4654	103,5	16,2	6,1	14	gen(372c)

(ex Aquitaine Spirit-97, CMBT Cutter-96, Emma-96, Rhein Lagan-94, Francop-94, Manchester Trader-92, Francop-91)

m.s. "Inka Dede" Friedhelm Dede KG								
INKA DEDE *(ATG)*	92	5006	6580	116,7	18,2	6,9	16	cc(520c)

(ex Armada Sprinter-96, Inka Dede-95, Rhein Liffey-94, Inka Dede-93)

m.s. "Jana" Holger und Herbert Szidat KG								
JANA *(ATG)*	90	3125	3070	89,1	16,2	4,8	15	gen(266c)
TESCH Bereederungsgesellschaft mbH & Co. KG m.s. "Katharina B"								
KATHARINA B *(DEU)*	97	3995	5865	100,0	18,2	6,6	16	cc(523c)

*The **JANA**, registered in the German port of Stade but flying the Antiguan flag, leaves Belfast on 1 July 1995.*
(Alan Geddes)

BILBERRY SHIPPING & STEVEDORES LTD.

Bilberry, Waterford, Co Waterford, Irish Republic (+353 51 872224/fax +353 51 879372)
Managers for:

Seal Sands Maritime Ltd								
SEAL SANDS *(VCT)*	63	1535	2419	84,7	14,1	4,4	10	sd
(ex Zeeland-92, Stone Marshall-77, Needwood-73)								
Sunwood Shipping Ltd								
SAND MARTIN *(VCT)*	63	540	650	53,1	9,3	3,5	9	sd
(ex Sand Lark-91)								
SAND SWIFT *(GBR)*	69	1204	1944	66,5	12,5	4,3	10	sd

BORCHARD LINES LTD

Durrant House, Chiswell Street, London, EC1Y 4XY (0171 628 6961/fax 0171)
Chartered tonnage:
m.s. "Inga Lena" Ludwig Rass KG
CHARLOTTE
BORCHARD *(DEU)* 97 6362 7225 121,4 18,5 6,7 16 cc(700c)
(ex Inga Lena-98, launched as Hoheriff)
Ernst-August von Allworden und Dirk Jaeger KG
JOANNA BORCHARD *(DEU)* 97 6362 7225 121,4 18,5 6,7 16 cc(700c)
(launched as Petuja)
m.s. "Sven" Wilfried Rambow KG
LUCY BORCHARD *(DEU)* 96 5309 7225 121,4 18,5 6,7 16 cc(700c)
(ex Solid-97, Sven-96)
m.s. "Kalina" Reederei Nagel KG
RACHEL BORCHARD *(DEU)* 96 5309 7225 121,4 18,5 6,7 16 cc(700c)
(ex Sound-97, completed as Kalina)
m.s. "Hohebank" Ludwig Rass KG
SUSAN BORCHARD *(DEU)* 96 6362 7223 121,4 18,5 6,7 16 cc(700c)
(ex Pentland-97, completed as Hohebank)
Note : See also CHARLES M. WILLIE & CO (SHIPPING) *for other chartered tonnage*

BP SHIPPING LTD.

Breakspear Park, Breakspear Way, Hemel Hempstead, Herts, HP2 4UL
(01442 232323/fax 01442 225225)
BRITISH TAMAR *(GBR)* 73 15163 25498 171,5 25,1 9,6 15 tk
Managers for:
BP Oil UK Ltd
BORDER BATTLER *(GBR)* 68 1410 2257 76,0 12,5 4,7 11 tk
(ex BP Battler-97, Inverness-76)
BORDER JOUSTER *(GBR)* 72 1568 2734 78,2 12,6 5,2 12 tk
(ex BP Jouster-97, Swansea-76)
BORDER SPRINGER *(GBR)* 69 1071 1538 65,5 11,3 4,5 11 tk
(ex BP Springer-97, Dublin-76)
BORDER WARRIOR *(GBR)* 68 1410 2257 76,0 12,5 4,7 11 tk
(ex BP Warrior-97, Grangemouth-76)

BR SHIPMANAGEMENT A/S

Kvaesthusgade 6A, 1251 Copenhagen, K, Denmark (+45 33364400/fax +45 33364401)
Managers for:
K/S Camilla
LADY CAMILLA *(IOM)* 73 1999 3310 93,3 14,0 5,4 12 ch tk
(ex Lubchem-98, Mobil Lubchem-91)

BRIGGS MARINE ENVIRONMENTAL SERVICES LTD

Leading Light Building, 142 Sinclair Road, Torry, Aberdeen, AB11 9PR
(01224 898666/ fax 01224 896950. E-mail: bmes@briggs marine.com)
Managers for:
Briggs Commercial Ltd
BRITISH SHIELD *(GBR)* 79 2804 3659 97,6 13,7 5,8 13 tk
(ex Oscona-97, Seneca-95)
Note : Employed on oil spill recovery standby

BRITANNIA AGGREGATES LTD.

Robert Brett House, Milton Manor Farm, Canterbury, Kent, CT4 7PP
(01227 829000/fax 01227 829039)
Managers for:

Natwest Leasing (GB) Ltd

BRITANNIA BEAVER	*(GBR)*	91	3610	5786	100,0	17,7	6,2	12	sd

BULLAS TANKCRAFT CO LTD.

Telegraph House, Telegraph Hill, Higham, Rochester, Kent, ME3 7MW
(01634 717509/fax 01634 295079)

CELTIC 4	*(IRL)* *	71	801	1392	69,4	9,0	3,0	11	tk bge
(ex Oiltrans 31-81)									
THAMES RAPID	*(GBR)*	74	589	670	58,9	10,3	2,6	10	tk bge
(ex Rapid-86, BP Rapid-86, Sheppey-76)									

*Note : * Vessel was unofficially renamed* RAPID II.

CAMPBELL MARITIME LTD.

Maritime House, 6, Coronation Street, South Shields, Tyne & Wear, NE33 1LA
(0191 427 0303/fax 0191 455 0790)
Managers for:

Giles W. Pritchard-Gordon & Co Ltd

ALICE PG	*(IOM)* *	94	3627	6248	102,1	16,1	6,5	12	tk
LESLEY PG	*(IOM)* *	98	3630	6249	102,1	16,1	6,5	12	tk

Franco British Chartering Agency Ltd

ARDENT	*(GBR)*	83	700	1180	50,0	9,5	3,6	9	gen
CORNET	*(BHS)*	76	892	1255	64,0	10,5	3,8	11	gen(52c)
(ex Daunt Rock-88)									
MILLAC STAR II	*(BHS)*	74	1596	1535	75,7	11,8	3,9	12	gen
(ex Emanaich-86, Caravelle-83)									
ROUSTEL	*(BHS)*	78	892	1240	64,0	10,5	3,7	11	gen(52c)
(ex Skellig Rock-88)									
TORRENT	*(GBR)*	91	999	1733	63,6	11,0	4,1	9	gen

*The **MILLAC STAR II** passes the ferry terminal at the Hook of Holland as she hurries up the New Waterway towards Rotterdam on 14 July 1997.* (Richard Potter)

Waveney Shipping PLC

CAROLE T	*(GBR)*	80	613	1120	49,6	9,5	3,9	9	gen

(ex Emily PG-93)

Celtic Tankers PLC

CELTIC TERRIER	*(GBR)*	79	7676	12905	142,4	17,8	8,6	14	ch tk

(ex United Terrier-93, Ilse-91)

Franco British Chartering Ltd & Singa Shipping Co Ltd

DOWLAIS	*(GBR)*	85	794	1394	58,3	9,4	3,9	8	gen

Partrederiet Eliza PG DA

ELIZA PG	*(IOM)* *	92	3338	5440	96,2	16,1	6,3	12	tk

Pritchard-Gordon Tankers Ltd

EMILY PG	*(IOM)* *	96	3627	6249	102,1	16,1	6,5	12	tk

Forth Tankers PLC

FORTH BRIDGE	*(GBR)*	92	3338	5800	96,2	16,1	6,6	12	tk

Note : * Currently engaged in Caribbean trading

CARISBROOKE SHIPPING PLC.

10 Mill Hill Road, Cowes, Isle of Wight, PO31 7EA (01983 284100 /fax 01983 290111)

CHERYL C	*(BRB)*	83	1636	2367	70,1	13,1	5,0	10	gen(70c)

(ex Catarina Caldas-91, Catarina-89, Norbrit Rijn-87, Norbrit Hope-85)

ELIZABETH C	*(BRB)*	71	2165	2823	85,0	12,8	5,1	13	gen

(ex Mark C-96, Mark-86, Security-86)

KLAZINA C	*(BRB)*	83	1548	2554	81,3	12,0	4,3	10	gen

(ex Lasina-88, Klazina H-88, Klazina-85)

MARY C	*(BRB)*	77	1522	2440	66,1	13,1	5,1	12	gen

(ex Fiducia-89, Ligato-88)

MINKA C	*(BRB)*	75	1655	2657	78,7	12,5	5,0	12	gen

(ex Victory-95)

VANESSA C	*(BRB)*	74	1853	3165	80,1	13,6	5,5	12	gen

(ex Vanessa-93)

Newbuilding (Damen-Hoogezand)

		99		5030				12	gen

Managers for :

Capital Bank Leasing (9) Ltd

ANJA C	*(BRB)*	91	2230	3222	99,7	12,6	4,3	10	gen(114c)

(ex Tima Saturn-92, launched as Union Saturn)

NORDSTRAND	*(BRB)*	91	1960	2800	88,3	12,5	4,6	11	gen(158c)

(ex Nicole-93)

Heleen Shipping & Edelweiss Shipping Ltd

HELEEN C	*(BRB)*	74	1472	2159	71,3	11,6	5,0	12	gen

(ex Luther-89, Irina-81)

CARISBROOKE SHIPPING (HOLLAND) B.V.

Postbus 30007, 3001 DA Rotterdam, Netherlands (+ 31 010 2056581)
Managers for:

Carisbrooke Shipping C.V.

EMILY C	*(BRB)*	96	2741	4650	89,8	13,2	6,0	11	gen(197c)
MARK C	*(BRB)*	96	2745	4619	89,8	13,2	6,0	11	gen(197c)
VECTIS ISLE	*(NLD)*	90	2230	3274	99,7	13,0	4,3	11	gen(114c)

(ex Lesley-Jane C-93, completed as Union Mercury)

CARISBROOKE SHIPPING (MANAGEMENT) LTD

10 Mill Hill Road, Cowes, Isle of Wight, PO31 7EA (01983 284100 /fax 01983 290111)
Managers for:

Carisbrooke Shipping C.V.4

JANET C *(GBR)*	98	2748	4290	89,9	13,2	6,0	11	gen(197c)

Carisbrooke Shipping C.V.3

JOHANNA C *(GBR)*	98	2748	4290	89,9	13,2	6,0	11	gen(197c)

Baybreak Ltd

TINA C *(BRB)*	74	1655	2591	78,7	12,3	5,0	12	gen

(ex Vanda-95)

Baybreak Ltd & Dynaship Maritime Ltd

VECTIS FALCON *(BRB)*	78	2351	3564	87,0	13,8	5,7	12	gen

(ex Fribourg-93, Clarknes-83)

*The **JOHANNA C** lies at Rotterdam's Parkkade on 26 June 1998, the day of her delivery.* (Harold Appleyard)

CELTIC MARINE LTD.

Eaglehurst, 64-64 Belmont Hill, Douglas, IoM, IM1 4NY (01624 620668/fax 01624 625557)
Managers for:

D.U.K. Shipping Ltd

NORTHERN STAR *(GBR)* *	80	1114	719	64,5	10,3	3,5	11	lpg(ch)

Note : * Laid up Manchester. Also managers for BELFAST FREIGHT FERRIES *qv*

CHANNEL ISLAND SHIP MANAGEMENT LTD.

21 Britannia Place, Bath Street, St Helier, Jersey, Channel Islands, JE2 4SU
(01534 58507/fax 01534 21284)
Managers for:

Channel Island Ferries Ltd

PURBECK *(BHS)*	78	6507	1550	125,5	17,5	4,5	18	ro(40u)

Note : Time chartered to FALCON SEAFREIGHT *qv*.

CLIFFGOLD LTD. trading as N. E. MURRAY MARINE CONTRACTORS

8 Rushenden Road, Queenborough , Kent, ME11 5BH (01795 580998/fax 01795 665534)
Managers for:

Sheridan Grange Ltd

CAPTION *(GBR)*	63	189	269	32,1	7,2	2,3	8	wt tkbge/gen

Lavington International Ltd

SEALAND TRADER	*(GBR)*	75	499	800	42,5	10,0	3,6	9	gen

(ex Island Swallow-96, Sealand Trader-87)

Bareboat charter:

Holyhead Towing Co Ltd

YEOMAN ROSE	*(BLZ)*	75	507	965	42,5	10,0	3,6	9	gen

(ex Island Swift-90, SeaborneTrader-87)

CLYDEPORT LTD

16 Robertson Street, Glasgow, G2 8DS (0141 221-8733/fax 0141 2488-3167)

Chartered tonnage:

Tinnes Panama SA

TINNES	*(PAN)*	83	6944	10110	117,7	20,6	8,5	14	bulk

(ex General Bonifacio-88, Tinnes-86)

COASTAL CONTAINER LINE LTD.

S.6 Berth, Royal Seaforth Container Terminal, Seaforth, Liverpool, L21 1JD
(0151 949-1000/fax 0151 949-10079)

Chartered tonnage:

Schiffahrtsgesellschaft J. Claussen KG

CHRISTOPHER

MEEDER	*(ATG)*	76	2154	2200	86,9	13,0	4,8	13	gen(135c)

Astor Schiffahrtsges mbH & Co KG m.s. "Markab J"

COASTAL BAY	*(ATG)*	91	2463	3269	87,4	13,0	5,1	12	gen(202c)

(ex Rhein Feeder-96, Rhein Lee-94, Rhein Feeder-93, Liesel I-91)

Kaduto Schiffahrtsgellschaft mbH & Co m.s. "Hanni J"

COASTAL BREEZE	*(ATG)*	90	2463	3200	87,4	13,1	5,1	12	gen(202c)

(ex Herm J-98. Cari-Star-94, Primo-92, Medeur Primo-92, Rhein Carrier-91, Herm J-90)

Partenreederei m.s. "Johanna"

COASTAL ISLE	*(DEU)*	91	3125	2973	89,1	16,2	6,1	14	gen(258c)

(ex Johanna-97)

Reederei Klaus Schneider KG

COASTAL SOUND	*(DEU)*	83	2046	1876	78,0	13,9	5,0	13	gen(124c)

(ex Kirsten-98, Christopher Caribe-93, Saturnus-92, Craigavad-88)

KG m.s. "Neptunus" Reederei Kolb GmbH & Co

COASTAL WAVE	*(DEU)*	83	2046	1880	78,0	13,9	5,0	13	gen(124c)

(ex Pellworm-98, Neptunus-95, Craigantlet-88)

COLT INDUSTRIAL SERVICES LTD.

Colt Business Park, Witty Street, Hull, HU3 4TT (01482 214244/fax 01482 215037)

BUSTARDTHORPE	*(GBR)*	14	77	98	28,0	5,2	2,0	7	gen bge
HUMBER MARINER	*(GBR)*	63	103	300	42,1	5,3	2,1	8	tk bge

COMMODORE FERRIES (CI) LTD.

PO Box 10, New Jetty Offices, White Rock, St Peter Port, Guernsey, GY1 3AF
(01481 728620/fax 01481 728521)

Newbuilding (Van der Giessen)

COMMODORE CLIPPER	Sep 99		3800		129,1	23,4	5,6	19	ro/px(93u/100a)

Time chartered:

NYDA Shipping L.P.

COMMODORE

GOODWILL	*(BHS)*	96	11166	5215	126,4	21,4	6,0	17	ro(94u)

KS Nordic Shipping

ISLAND COMMODORE	*(BHS)*	95	11166	5215	126,4	21,4	5,8	18	ro(94u)

The **ISLAND COMMODORE** at anchor off Spithead on 25 June 1995.　　　　(Chris Bancroft)

CONCORDE CONTAINER LINE
The Innovation Centre, Staffordshire Technology Park, Beaconside, Stafford, ST18 0AR
(01785 212164/ fax 01785 212165)
Chartered tonnage:
  Compagnie Naviere San Gilles S.A.
DALHEM *(PAN)*　　　　　　　77　　2581　　2937　　88,4　　15,8　　4,8　　13　　gen(220c)
  (ex Sabine D-96, Gustav Behrmann-89, Contship Two-79, Gustav Behrmann-77)

CORNISH CALCIFIED SEAWEED CO LTD.
Newham Industrial Estate, Newham Road, Truro, Cornwall, TR1 2SU
(01872 278878/ fax 01872 225555)
DICTION *(GBR)*　　　　　63　　　189　　　254　　32,1　　7,2　　2,3　　7　　sd
GOOLE STAR *(GBR)* *　　70　　　210　　　375　　33,5　　6,6　　2,7　　7　　sd
Note : The company dredges and markets calcified seaweed.　　*　refitting at Truro

C. CRAWLEY LTD.
Town Pier, West Street, Gravesend, Kent, DA11 0BN (01474 365244 /fax 01474 320673)
AQUATIC *(GBR)*　　　　　63　　　199　　　315　　35,1　　7,5　　2,3　　7　　wt tk bge
  (ex Busby-85)
AQUEDUCT *(GBR)*　　　　64　　　594　　　908　　62,3　　10,2　　3,0　　10　　tk
  (ex Charcrest-91)
BRUCE STONE *(GBR)*　　64　　　357　　　375　　43,7　　9,2　　2,3　　8　　tk
  (ex Viaduct-78, Bruce Stone-76)
K/TOULSON *(GBR)*　　　66　　　614　　　833　　52,9　　10,3　　3,8　　9　　tk
  (ex Beechcroft-90)
MARPOL *(GBR)*　　　　　57　　　200　　　360　　36,6　　6,5　　2,6　　8　　tk
  (ex Snydale H)
TOMMY *(GBR)*　　　　　　63　　　217　　　315　　35,1　　7,5　　2,3　　8　　tk
  (ex Batsman-87)
TORDUCT *(GBR)*　　　　59　　　　65　　　100　　28,1　　5,3　　2,1　　8　　tk bge
  (ex Wakefield-70)

CRESCENT MARINE SERVICES LTD.

Crescent House, Otterham Quay Lane, Rainham, Gillingham, Kent, ME8 7UN
(01634 360077/fax 01634 387500)
Managers for:
Thames Water Utilities Ltd

BEXLEY *(GBR)*	66	2175	2471	89,9	15,1	4,1	12	sludge
HOUNSLOW *(GBR)*	68	2132	2471	89,9	15,2	4,1	12	sludge

The company is a wholly owned subsidiary of Crescent Plc
Note : vessels laid up on River Thames pending sale

CRESCENT SHIPPING LTD.

Address and details as above
Operators for:
Crescent Navigation Ltd

AMBIENCE *(BHS)*	83	664	1020	59,6	9,3	3,2	9	gen
BOISTERENCE *(BHS)*	83	664	1020	59,6	9,3	3,2	10	gen
CRESCENCE *(BHS)*	82	664	1020	59,6	9,3	3,2	10	gen
KINDRENCE *(BHS)*	76	2206	3210	91,2	13,5	5,1	10	gen
LUMINENCE *(BHS)*	77	1928	3210	91,3	13,5	5,1	10	gen
STRIDENCE *(BHS)*	83	1426	1821	84,7	11,5	3,4	10	gen
TARQUENCE *(BHS)*	80	664	1020	59,6	9,3	3,2	10	gen
TURBULENCE *(BHS)*	83	1426	1821	84,8	11,5	3,5	10	gen
URGENCE *(BHS)*	81	1425	1842	84,8	11,5	3,4	10	gen(80c)
VIBRENCE *(BHS)*	81	1425	1842	84,8	11,5	3,4	10	gen

The company is a wholly owned subsidiary of Crescent Plc

CRESCENT TANKSHIPS LTD.

Address and details as above
Managers for:

BANWELL *(GBR)*	80	1023	1710	71,9	11,1	3,7	10	tk
BARDSEY *(GBR)*	81	1144	1767	69,5	11,8	4,3	10	tk
(ex Sten-86)								
BARMOUTH *(GBR)*	80	1144	1774	69,5	11,8	4,3	10	tk
(ex Per-86)								
BLACKFRIARS *(GBR)*	85	992	1570	69,9	11,3	3,8	10	tk
BLACKHEATH *(GBR)*	80	751	1230	60,0	11,3	3,4	11	tk
BLACKROCK *(GBR)*	89	1646	2675	78,5	12,7	4,9	10	tk
BRABOURNE *(GBR)*	89	1646	2675	78,5	12,7	4,9	10	tk
BREAKSEA *(GBR)*	85	992	1570	69,9	11,3	3,8	10	tk
BRENTWOOD *(GBR)*	80	1004	1640	69,8	11,3	3,8	11	tk

The company is a wholly owned subsidiary of Crescent plc
Note : management of the fleet is undertaken by CRESCENT MARINE SERVICES *qv*

DALRIADA SHIPPING LTD.

Old Customs House, West Pier, Maritime Quarter, Swansea, West Glamorgan, SA1 1UN
(01792 655300/fax 01792 642508)

BURE *(PAN)*	69	347	610	44,4	7,9	3,2	9	gen
(ex Cadence-85)								

DART LINE LTD.

Thames Europort, Dartford, Kent, DA2 6QA (01322 281122/fax 01322 281133)
Chartered tonnage:
Octogon Shipping & Services

DART 1 *(ROM)*	84	9071	4830	120,0	21,0	5,3	15	ro(80u)
(ex Jolly Arancione-97, Bazias 1-96, Balder Fjord-86)								

"C.N.M. ROMLINE" Shipping Co S.A.

DART 2 *(ROM)*		84	9080	4700	120,0	21,0	5,3	15	ro(80u)
(ex Bazias 2-95, Balder Hav-85)									
DART 5 *(ROM)*		86	9082	4700	120,0	21,0	5,3	15	ro(80u)
(ex Perseus-96, Bazias 5-95, launched as Balder Ra)									
Estonian Shipping Co (ESCO)(RAS Eesti Merelaevandus)									
LEMBITU *(EST)* +		98	7606	5758	122,3	19,8	6,2	17	ro(70u)
VARBOLA *(EST)* ++		98	7606	5758	122,3	19,8	6,2	17	ro(70u)

Note : To be renamed early 1999   + DART 7   ++ DART 6

JOANNA DAVIS.

Norton Curlew Manor, Hatton, Warwick, CV35 8XQ (01926 842227/fax 01926 843314)

EILEAN EISDEAL *(GBR)* *		44	96	138	20,3	5,6	2,0	7	gen
(ex Eldesa-84, VIC 72)									

Note : * Laid up Island of Easdale

DEAN & DYBALL SHIPPING LTD.

Ocean House, Drivers Wharf, 240 Northam Road, Southampton,SO14 0QD
(01703 233366/fax 01703 234246)

DOUGLAS McWILLIAM *(GBR)*	83	172	200	30,3	8,1	2,1	7	sludge

Note : Laid up Plymouth

DEAN'S TUGS & WORKBOATS LTD.

10 Wentworth Way, Hull, HU9 2AX (01482 219277/0860 301116)

GEORGE ODEY *(GBR)*	71	210	300	37,7	6,7	2,4	7	gen bge
HUMBER MONARCH *(GBR)*	78	230	400	43,3	6,7	2,4	7	gen bge
JOLLY MINER *(GBR)*	70	165	360	47,9	5,5	2,1	7	gen bge
MAUREEN ANN *(GBR)*	62	207	380	34,4	6,6	2,4	8	gen bge
RISBY *(GBR)*	68	186	300	39,6	5,5	2,1	8	gen bge

DENHOLM SHIP MANAGEMENT (I.O.M.) LTD.

PO Box 200, Circular Road, Douglas, IoM, IM99 1DH (01624 626582/fax 01624 624445)
Managers for:

Manx Car Carriers Ltd

CITY OF BARCELONA *(IOM)*	93	9576	2402	99,9	20,6	5,0	15	vc(806a)
CITY OF SUNDERLAND *(IOM)*	93	9576	2417	99,9	20,6	5,0	16	vc(806a)

DENVAL MARINE CONSULTANTS LTD.

156 High Street, Sevenoaks, Kent, TN13 1XE (01732 458288/fax 01732 458277)

PRIMROSE *(CYP)*		75	6276	2039	118,4	23,0	4,5	22	ro/px(50u)
(ex Princesse Marie Christine-98)									

Managers/agents for:

Chartwell Navigation Co Ltd

ROSEANNE *(CYP)*		82	7744	4106	112,8	18,7	6,4	14	ro(80u)
(ex Faroy-89, Reina del Cantabrico-87, Salah Labiad-85, Reina del Cantabrico-83)									

Maritime Co Ltd

ROSEBAY *(CYP)*	76	13700	5233	135,5	21,8	6,1	17	ro(100u)
(ex Eurocruiser-98, Eurostar-97, Rosebay-97, Transgermania-93)								

DFM LTD.

Suite 73, Waszyngtona 34/36, 81-342 Gdynia, Poland (+ 48 58 627 6251/fax + 48 58 627 6250)
Managers for:

K/S UL Fetish

FETISH *(CYM)*	77	3136	4240	94,4	15,5	6,0	13	gen(150c)

K/S UL Magic								
MAGIC *(CYM)*	83	3134	3960	94,2	15,5	6,0	13	gen(130c)
K/S UL Medallion								
MEDALLION *(CYM)*	81	3136	4102	94,2	15,5	5,9	13	gen(130c)
K/S UL Scarab								
SCARAB *(CYM)*	83	3136	4240	94,2	15,5	5,8	13	gen(130c)

DGW SAND CO.
Sandbank, 22 Sandyacres Road, Loggans, Hayle, Cornwall, TR27 5BA
(01736 752961/fax 01736 757024)

COEDMOR *(GBR)*	46	181	244	32,9	6,1	2,6	7	sd
(ex Arran Monarch-64, Vic 47-48)								
SANDIE *(GBR)*	58	199	350	32,6	7,2	2,9	9	sd
(ex Sjobjorn VIII-90, Sandie, Wargon IV)								

DORCHESTER MARITIME LTD.
Thornton House, Belmont Hill, Douglas, Isle of Man, IM1 4RE
(01624 631800/fax 01624 626020)
Managers for:

Dale Ltd								
DOROTHEA SCHULTE *(NIS)*	81	4884	6113	110,9	15,5	7,5	14	lpg
Monet Trading Ltd								
HERMANN SCHULTE *(NIS)*	80	4884	6137	110,9	15,5	7,5	14	lpg

ONESIMUS DOREY (SHIPOWNERS) LTD.
La Salerie House, St Peter Port, PO Box 33, Guernsey, C.I.
The company is a wholly owned subsidiary of JAMES FISHER & SONS PUBLIC LIMITED COMPANY.
See also F. T. EVERARD & SONS MANAGEMENT, JAMES FISHER & SONS (LIVERPOOL) and TORBULK.

DRAGON SHIPPING LINE
F Berth, King's Dock, Swansea, West Glamorgan,SA1 (01792 458854/fax 01792 456605)
Agents only for:

Vogelsang-Bereederungs KG m.s "Jan V"								
JAN-V *(DEU)*	85	1749	2218	80,7	12,6	4,2	12	gen(142c)

CORPORATION OF DUBLIN (Bardas Atha Cliath)
City Hall, Cork Hill, Dublin, Irish Republic (+ 3531 679 6111/fax + 3531 679 0809)
SIR JOSEPH

BAZALGETTE *(IRL)*	63	2258	2187	89,5	14,2	12,8	12	sludge

EAST COAST FERRIES LTD. (ECF)
Queen Elizabeth Dock, Hull HU9 5PB (01482 715235/fax 01482 715341)
Chartered tonnage:

Eptanisos Maritime Ltd								
LOON PLAGE *(CYP)*	91	4962	4500	136,0	20,5	6,7	20	ro(75u)
(ex Kosei Maru-98)								
Octogon Shipping & Services								
OCTOGON 3 *(ROM)*	84	9983	6704	140,1	23,5	7,2	14	
ro(75u/289c)								
(ex Tutova-96, launched as Ritzberg)								

EAST OF SCOTLAND WATER
597 Calder Road, Edinburgh, EH11 4HJ (0131 553-9201/fax 0131 553-9269)

GARDYLOO *(GBR)*	76	1876	2695	85,9	14,2	4,7	12	sludge

EFFLUENTS SERVICES LTD. (ESL)
140 Moss Lane, Macclesfield, Cheshire, SK11 7YT (01625 429666/fax 01625 511305)

GREENDALE H *(GBR)*	62	311	536	43,1	6,7	3,1	7	sludge

EKTANK AB
PO Box 2521, 403 17 Gothenburg, Sweden (+ 46 031 609250/fax + 46 031 7114857)
Managers for:
Turus Shipping Ltd

EKFORS *(IOM)*	75	5529	9927	126,8	17,2	7,9	13	ch tk

ELF EXPLORATION (UK) Plc.
Bales Industrial Estate, Peterhead, Aberdeenshire, AB42 7JF (01779 871200/fax 01779 871292)
Chartered tonnage:
Interessentskabet Jentrader II

JENTRADER *(DIS)*	68	520	710	49,7	8,3	3,5	11	gen
(ex Marlin-79, Charles Trigon-75, Anna-Regil-70)								

EUCON SHIPPING & TRANSPORT LTD.
Breakwater Road, Alexander Road, Dublin 2, Irish Republic (+353 1 8552222/fax +353 1 8552311)
Chartered tonnage:
Condra Schiffahrts GmbH & Co KG m.s. "Gertrud"

EMMA *(ATG)*	96	4628	5660	113,0	16,4	6,1	16	cc(510c)
(ex Gertrud-96)								
m.s. "Karin" Egon Kopke KG								
JANE *(DEU)*	97	6362	7223	121,4	18,5	6,7	16	cc(700c)
(ex Karin-98)								
Reedereiges m.s. "Komet" Henry Gerdau KG GmbH & Co								
PLANET V *(DEU)*	94	4984	7014	116,4	19,5	7,1	16	gen(532c)
(ex Gracechurch Planet-97, Planet V-96)								
Partenreederei m.s. "Partnership"								
YVETTE *(DEU)*	96	6362	7225	121,4	18,5	6,7	16	cc(700c)
(ex Partnership-96)								

Note: The company is a trading name of Irish Continental Group PLC., Dublin.
Chartered and operated by:
HUDIG & KERSTEN CONTINENT IRELAND LINE B.V.
Kapitan Manfred Draxl Schiffahrts GmbH & Co KG m.v. "Dorte"

MATHILDA *(ATG)*	94	3958	5350	108,0	16,0	6,0	16	cc(448c)
(ex Dorte-94)								

EUROFEEDERS LTD.
Suite 14a, Orwell House, Ferry Lane, Felixstowe, Suffolk, IP11 8QL
(01394 676667/fax 01394 675606)
Chartered tonnage:
m.s. "Anja II" Schiffahrtsges. mbH & Co.

ANJA II *(ATG)*	91	2705	3982	89,5	13,5	5,3	12	gen(220c)
Clonakilty Shipping Ltd								
CAMIRA *(IRL)*	97	4107	4800	100,5	16,2	6,4	14	gen(374c)
m.s. "Connemara" Emerald Isle Containers Ltd								
CONNEMARA *(IRL)*	97	4107	4800	100,5	16,2	6,4	14	gen(374c)
Partrederiet for m.s. "Weser"								
WESER *(DIS)*	74	2709	3981	93,2	14,6	6,2	14	gen(195c)

*The **CONNEMARA** heads up Southampton Water on 17 September 1998 during one of her regular voyages linking Belfast and Dublin to Southampton, Felixstowe and Thamesport.* *(Chris Bancroft)*

EUROLINE SHIPPING CO. LTD.
Dock Gate House, Waterloo Quay, Aberdeen, AB11 5DF
(011224 595999/fax 01224 593444. E-mail: info@euroline-shipping.co.uk)
Agents only for tonnage chartered for Rulewave North Sea Service:

Marsani Shipping Co N.V.

AURIGA *(ANT)*	78	1589	1670	84,2	10,8	3,7	10	gen(63c)
(ex Algerak-90, Germann-86)								

Rederij Bamestra

ROBETA *(NLD)*	85	1372	1570	75,1	10,8	3,8	11	gen
(ex Beta-98)								

Barrack Trading Ltd

RULEWAVE								
WARRIOR *(BHS)*	78	1307	1426	84,9	9,5	3,3	10	gen(69c)
(ex Topaz-95, Aramon-94, Markab-86)								

*The **AURIGA** photographed outward bound in the River Ouse on 10 June 1995.* *(David H Smith)*

EUROSHIP SERVICES LTD.

Purfleet Deep Wharf, London Road, Purfleet, Essex, RM19 1RP
(01708 891166/fax 01708 891177. E-mail: euroship@dial.pipex.com)
Managing agents for COBELFRET owned tonnage. Purfleet Agency Ltd are marketing and sales for
Purfleet-Zeebrugge and Exxtor Ltd for Immingham-Zeebrugge/Rotterdam:

Euroship Services Ltd & Belcan N.V.

AMANDINE *(GBR)*	78	14715	14043	173,0	21,7	7,6	15	ro(120u/100a)

(ex Vega-98, Bruarfoss-96, Persia-88, Merzario Persia-86)

Novomar S.A.

CLEMENTINE *(LUX)*	97	23986	9655	162,5	25,6	6,5	17	ro(150u/550a)

Coburg S.A.

CYMBELINE *(LUX)*	92	11866	6500	147,0	21,0	5,3	17	ro(100u/275a)
LOVERVAL *(LUX)*	78	10931	9019	161,4	18,0	6,7	17	ro(95u/80a)

(ex Matina-85, Vallmo-83)

UNDINE *(LUX)*	91	11854	6500	147,4	21,0	5,3	15	ro(100u/275a)

Somarlux S.A.

EGLANTINE *(LUX)*	90	10035	7225	147,4	21,0	5,3	14	ro(100u/275a)
SYMPHORINE *(LUX)*	88	10030	7154	147,4	21,0	5,3	14	ro(100u/275a)

Oceanarrow Ltd Inc.

SEA CRUSADER *(GBR)* *	96	23986	9677	162,5	25,6	6,5	18	ro(150u/550a)

(Completed as Celestine)

New building (2)	99	23986	9677	162,5	25,6	6,5	19	ro(157u/550a)

Chartered tonnage:

Lyra Line Ltd

LYRA *(ATG)*	78	12817	9855	172,0	21,6	6,6	15	ro(120u/100a)

(ex Silkeborg-97, Laxfoss-96, Duino-88, Jolly Ocra-87, Merzario Arabia-86)

DFDS A/S

DANA HAFNIA *(DIS)*	79	11125	8538	161,4	18,0	6,7	16	ro(121u/542a)

Chartered tonnage for The Ford Motor Co Ltd, Dagenham contract:

Dag Engstrom Rederi A/B

RODONA *(SWE)*	80	6568	3085	136,1	16,5	4,7	14	ro(75u/300a)

(ex Balder Dona-84)

SAPPHIRE *(SWE)*	80	6568	4538	136,1	16,5	4,7	14	ro(75u/300a)

(ex Azua-87, Rovinga-84, Balder Vinga-84)

Note : * *Chartered to the Royal Fleet Auxiliary. See also* MAERSK (IOM) *and* NORTHERN
MARINE MANAGEMENT

*The **SYMPHORINE** is a regular visitor to the River Thames. She is seen approaching that river on 1 October 1997.*
(Barry Standerline)

F. T. EVERARD & SONS LTD.

The Wharf, Greenhithe, Kent, DA9 9NW (01322 382345/fax 01322 383422)

ABILITY *(GBR)*	79	1696	2550	79,3	13,2	5,0	13	oil/veg tk
AUTHENTICITY *(GBR)*	79	1696	2550	79,3	13,2	4,9	12	oil/veg tk
SAGACITY *(BHS)*	73	1926	3238	91,3	13,3	5,1	12	gen
SPECIALITY *(BHS)*	77	2822	4245	89,7	14,3	6,0	12	gen(122c)
STABILITY *(BHS)*	78	2822	4245	91,1	14,3	6,4	12	gen(122c)
Managers for:								
F. T. Everard Shipping Ltd								
AGILITY *(GBR)*	90	1930	3144	80,0	14,6	5,6	11	tk
ALACRITY *(GBR)*	90	1930	3145	80,0	14,6	5,6	12	tk
AMITY *(BHS)*	80	1147	1767	69,5	11,8	4,3	11	tk
(ex Christian-88)								
ANNUITY *(GBR)*	88	1711	3294	83,5	13,5	5,5	10	tk
(ex Janne Terkol-95)								
ASPERITY *(GBR)*	97	2965	3778	88,6	16,5	5,6	13	tk
AUDACITY *(GBR)*	97	2965	3778	88,6	16,5	5,6	13	tk
AVERITY *(BHS)*	81	1144	1770	69,5	11,8	4,3	11	tk
(ex Natalie-88)								
SANGUITY *(GBR)*	84	1892	2887	79,0	12,7	5,1	10	gen(94c)
(ex Willonia-88)								
SOCIALITY *(GBR)*	86	1892	2887	79,0	12,8	5,1	10	gen(94c)
(ex Stevonia-87)								
3i PLC								
AMENITY *(GBR)*	80	1696	2528	79,2	13,2	5,0	13	tk
PAMELA EVERARD *(GBR)*	84	1892	2887	79,0	12,7	5,1	10	gen(94c)
SELECTIVITY *(GBR)*	84	1892	2887	79,0	12,7	5,1	10	gen(94c)
Hadley Shipping Co Ltd								
COTINGA *(BHS)*	76	1921	3089	83,5	14,1	5,2	11	gen
Short Sea Europe PLC								
NORTH SEA TRADER *(GBR)*	91	2230	3222	99,7	12,5	4,3	11	gen(114c)
SHORT SEA TRADER *(GBR)*	91	2230	3263	99,7	12,5	4,3	10	gen(114c)

The **NORTH SEA TRADER** waits off the Alfred Lock entrance, Birkenhead, on 1 May 1997.

(Ambuscade Marine Photography)

Scottish Navigation Co Ltd

SENIORITY	*(GBR)*	91	3493	5163	99,5	16,6	5,4	11	gen
SUPERIORITY	*(GBR)*	91	2230	3212	100,0	12,5	4,3	11	gen(114c)

F. T. EVERARD & SONS MANAGEMENT LTD.
4 Elder Street, London, E1 6DD (0171 247-8181/fax 0171 377-5562)
Freight managers for:

D. J. Goubert Shipping Ltd

CANDOURITY	*(GBR)*	75	559	880	56,1	9,9	3,2	10	gen
LANCRESSE	*(GBR)*	75	534	716	49,7	8,3	3,5	10	gen

(ex Jenstar-97, Trojborg-95, Platessa-91)

Faversham Ships Ltd

CONFORMITY	*(GBR)*	75	559	880	56,1	9,9	3,2	11	gen

Onesimus Dorey (Shipowners) Ltd demise chartered to **Torbulk Ltd**, Grimsby

PENTLAND	*(BRB)*	80	909	1315	60,0	11,3	3,9	12	gen

(ex Capacity-94, Lizzonia-89)

Note : F. T. Everard & Sons *are also freight managers/agents for vessels listed under other owners*

EXCEL CONTAINER LINE LTD.
Unit 5, Swanscombe Business Centre, 17 London Road, Swanscombe, Kent, DA10 0LH
(01322 386666/fax 01322 385555)
Chartered tonnage:

Partenreederei Bargte

BIANCA	*(ATG)*	72	1934	1531	77,02	13,03	4,2	13	gen(102c)

(ex Atria-86)

Sea Lazer Shipping Co Ltd

CHRISTIAN	*(CYP)*	77	2089	2461	86,5	12,8	4,9	13	gen(195c)

(ex Alita-95)

*The **CHRISTIAN** was photographed in the Firth of Forth on 1 August 1998.* *(E Dryden)*

FALCON SEAFREIGHT LTD.
Freight Office, Folkestone Harbour, Folkestone, Kent, CT20 1QH
(01303 221456/fax 01303 248709)
Chartered tonnage:

Hoverspeed (UK) Ltd

PICASSO	*(CYM)*	77	5669	2840	115,1	17,5	5,3	17	ro(35u)

(ex Poker-95, Beaverdale-91, Wuppertal-87, Canaima-79, Wuppertal-78)

See CHANNEL ISLAND SHIP MANAGEMENT *for other chartered tonnage.*

FALMOUTH OIL SERVICES (1994) LTD.

The Docks, Falmouth, Cornwall, TR11 4NJ (01326 211333/fax 01326 312989)

FALMOUTH
ENDEAVOUR *(GBR)* +   72   754   1276   62,7   9,8   4,2   11   bk tk
(ex Marwah II-87)

FALMOUTH
ENTERPRISE *(GBR)* +   72   1287   2189   76,0   11,2   5,1   11   bk tk
(ex Brady Maria-87, Hama Maru No 5-84)

Tonnage provided by the Whitaker Group:

John H. Whitaker (Tankers) Ltd

FALMOUTH
ENDURANCE *(GBR)* +   64   171   420   45,2   6,0   2,1   9   tk bge
(ex Humber Navigator-89)

FALMOUTH ENERGY *(GBR)* *   63   165   275   42,1   5,3   2,1   7   tk bge
(ex Rufus Stone-89)

FALMOUTH INDUSTRY *(GBR)*   61   257   500   44,0   6,3   2,4   8   tk bge
(ex Ulster Industry-89)

Twin Town Shipping Co Ltd

WHITONIA   *(BHS)*   77   2002   3153   83,0   14,3   5,9   13   bk tk
(ex Mare Aurum-98, Mare Novum-93)

*Note : +   Laid by at Falmouth pending sale.   *   Laid up.*

FARMERS FERRY LTD.

PO Box No.1, Portishead, Bristol, BS20 9BR (0870 2410153)

Chartered tonnage:

Delom S.A.

CAP AFRIQUE   *(ATF)*   78   1583   2401   108,6   16,3   5,0   17   ro(45u)
(ex Saint Charles-90, Catherine Schiaffino-89)

FEEDERLINK SHIPPING & TRADING B.V.

PO Box 53050, 3008 HB, Rotterdam, Netherlands (+ 31 10 491 26 66/fax + 31 10 429 52 05

Chartered tonnage:

m.s. "Ketty Brovig" Schiffahrtsgeseselschaft mbH & Co

KETTY BROVIG   *(NIS)*   84   3329   4115   98,7   15,5   5,4   14   gen(332c)
(ex Rockabill-98, Hasselwerder-94, Gracechurch Crown-90, Hasselwerder-89, City of Manchester-85, Hasselwerder-84)

m.s. "Pavo" Rohden Schiffahrts GmbH & Co

PAVO   *(ATG)*   86   3300   4107   92,4   15,7   6,0   14   gen(321c)
(ex Seevetal-98)

*The **PAVO** photographed passing Calshot Spit in November 1998.*   *(Philip Kempsey)*

Herman Buss KG m.s. "Western Trader"
WESTERN TRADER *(ATG)*   91   4164   4750   111,1   16,1   6,0   14   gen(381c)
(ex Gracechurch Meteor-97, completed as Western Trader)
Note : *The company is a wholly owned subsidiary of* Irish Continental Group PLC.

W. FIELDGATE & SON LTD.
Haven Quay, Colchester, Essex, CO2 8JE (01206 865432 /fax 01206 866104)
Agents only for:
Seatrade Ltd
RAIDER *(VCT)*   66   224   378   41,6   7,7   2,3   8   gen
(ex Anglian Trader-90, Lee James-82, Target Venture-78, Sheena K-78, Lady Sheena-76)

FINBETA S.p.A.
Via Nazionale Piemonte 4, 17100, Savona SV, Italy (+019 822780/fax +019 823703)
ACQUAMARINA *(IOM)*   88   3533   6058   117,6   15,8   6,1   14   ch tk
CRISTALLO *(IOM)*   91   5038   8091   125,2   17,4   7,1   14   ch tk
SAPPHIRE *(IOM)*   97   9914   14015   142,5   22,0   8,4   14   oil/ch tk
Newbuilding (Morini)   Late 99   7100   oil/ch tk

FINNANGLIA FERRIES LTD.
(Finncarriers/Andrew Weir), 8 Heron Quay, London, E14 4JB (0171 519 7300/fax 0171 536 0255)
Chartered tonnage:
OY Bore Lines AB
FINNBIRCH *(SWE)*   76   15396   8672   156,0   23,0   7,3   17   ro(140u/642c)
(ex Bore Gothica-97, Stena Gothica-88, Stena Ionia-85, Merzario Ionia-82, Stena Ionia-81,
Atlantic Prosper-81)
Baltic Marine Services AB
FINNFOREST *(SWE)*   78   15525   8800   151,0   22,7   7,3   17   ro(140u/642c)
(ex Bore Britannica-96, Stena Britannica-88, Stena Hispania-86, Kotka Violet-85, Stena Hispania-84,
Merzario Hispania-83, Atlantic Project-81)
Finnlines OY
FINNMASTER *(FIN)*   73   11839   5710   137,5   22,4   6,6   17   ro(112u/290c)
(ex Fennia-92, Sirius-87)
B&N Nordsjofrakt AB
FINNRIVER *(SWE)*   79   20172   12200   165,2   25,9   8,0   16   ro(120u/800c)
(ex Celia-96, Hesperus-86, Vasaland-83)
FINNROSE *(FIN)*   78   20169   12200   165,2   25,9   7,8   16   ro(120u/800c)
(ex Cortia-96, Hektos-86, Timmerland-84)

JAMES FISHER & SONS PUBLIC LIMITED COMPANY
Fisher House, PO Box 4, Barrow-in-Furness, Cumbria, LA14 1HR
(01229 822323/fax 01229 836761)
FURNESS FISHER *(GBR)*   55   1721   2464   97,5   11,9   2,6   9   bk tk bge
(ex Nordicus One-89)
NEW GENERATION *(GBR)*   66   2330   2233   86,7   16,5   4,6   11   ro h/l
(ex Kingsnorth Fisher-90)
Managers for:
British Nuclear Fuels Ltd
EUROPEAN
SHEARWATER *(GBR)*   81   2493   1583   80,0   12,6   5,1   11   nuc
(ex Mediterranean Shearwater-94)
ONESIMUS DOREY (SHIPOWNERS) LTD, JAMES FISHER & SONS (LIVERPOOL) LTD, JAMES
FISHER TANKSHIPS LTD and JAMES FISHER (GIBRALTAR) LTD *are wholly owned subsidiary
companies.*

JAMES FISHER & SONS (LIVERPOOL) LTD.

6th Floor, Martins Building, Water Street, Liverpool, L2 3UJ (0151 227-5531/fax 0151 236-2269)

BRIARTHORN	(GBR)	80	1576	2435	74,6	12,9	4,9	12	gen
(ex Craigallian-89)									
REDTHORN	(GBR)	78	2025	3070	85,3	13,8	5,0	12	gen
(ex Pinewood-90)									
ROSETHORN	(GBR)	82	1213	1694	69.3	11,1	4,3	11	gen(60c)
(ex Shamrock Endeavour-90)									
SILVERTHORN	(GBR)	82	1213	1694	69,3	11,1	4,3	11	gen(60c)
(ex Shamrock Enterprise-90)									
SOLWAY FISHER	(IRL)	77	1707	2703	73,3	13,2	5,1	11	gen(30c)
(ex Rockpoint-96, Arklow Valley-91, Procyon-84)									

Managers for:

Onesimus Dorey (Shipowners) Ltd

ROCKFLEET	(IRL)		79	1095	1622	66,2	11,5	4,5	11	gen
(ex Globe-93)										
ROCKISLAND	(IRL)	*	78	1279	1467	80,4	10,1	3,3	11	gen(47c)
(ex Verena-92)										
SEA BOYNE	(IRL)		77	1917	2192	79,1	12,4	4,8	12	gen(104c)
(ex Rockabill-93, Sybille-91, Echo Carrier-89, Scot Venture-88, Sybille-88)										

Note: * Laid over in Manchester

The company is a wholly owned subsidiary of JAMES FISHER & SONS Public Limited Companyqv

JAMES FISHER TANKSHIPS LTD.

Fourth Floor, 7 Birchin Lane, London, EC3V 9BY (0171 338 5800/fax 0171 338 5850)

FORTH FISHER	(GBR)	97	3368	3628	91,0	15,6	5,0	12	tk
(Launched as Quarterman)									
GALWAY FISHER	(GBR)	97	3368	3622	91,0	15,6	5,0	12	tk
(Launched as Wheelsman)									
MILFORD FISHER	(GBR)	98	3368	3627	91,0	15,6	5,1	12	tk
SOLENT FISHER	(GBR)	98	3368	3700	91,0	15,6	5,0	12	tk
(Launched as Bridgeman)									

The **GALWAY FISHER** leaves the Cattewater Harbour, Plymouth, on 15 June 1998.   (David Warren)

Operators for:

James Fisher & Sons Public Limited Company

TILLERMAN *(GIB)*	75	7686	12800	142,5	17,8	8,6	12	tk
(ex Thuntank 2-89, Inga-83)									

James Fisher (Gibraltar) Ltd

EASTGATE *(GIB)*	79	2072	3415	93,2	13,4	5,3	12	tk
IRISHGATE *(GIB)*	81	2071	3290	93,2	13,4	5,2	12	tk
LOUGH FISHER *(GIB)*	80	4777	8496	117,2	17,5	7,2	12	tk
(ex Cableman-98)									
NORTHGATE *(GIB)*	81	2071	3290	93,2	13,4	5,2	12	tk
OARSMAN *(GIB)*	80	1449	2547	76,1	12,5	4,9	10	tk
SEVERN FISHER *(GIB)*	83	5646	11250	119,7	19,2	8,1	11	tk
(ex Tankerman-98)									
STELLAMAN *(GIB)*	80	2804	3680	97,8	13,8	5,8	12	ch tk
(ex Navajo-94, Richard-88)									
WESTGATE *(GIB)*	79	2072	3368	93,2	13,6	5,3	12	tk

James Fisher & Sons (Liverpool) Ltd

HUMBER FISHER *(GBR)*	98	2760	4763	91,4	15,6	6,0	12	tk
MERSEY FISHER *(GBR)*	98	2760	4500	91,4	15,6	6,0	12	tk
TEES FISHER *(GBR)*	80	2077	3120	82,0	15,0	5,8	14	tk
(ex Michael M-99, BP Hunter-91)									
THAMES FISHER *(GBR)*	97	2760	4781	91,4	15,5	6,0	12	tk
TYNE FISHER *(GBR)*	80	1803	2924	75,2	13,3	5,8	12	ch tk
(ex Frederick M-98)									
WEAR FISHER *(GBR)*	80	2077	3120	82,0	15,0	5,8	14	oil/ch tk
(ex David M-98, BP Harrier-91)									

Bareboat chartered tonnage:

Nordenhamer Chemikalien und Produkten Transport GmbH m.t. "Antares" KG.

ANCHORMAN *(LBR)*	93	4842	6417	101,6	17,5	6,9	12	tk

Nordenhamer Chemikalien und Produkten Transport GmbH m.v. "Chartsman" KG.

CHARTSMAN *(LBR)*	93	4842	6397	101,6	17,5	6,9	12	tk

Nordenhamer Chemikalien und Produkten Transport GmbH m.t. "Rudderman" KG.

RUDDERMAN *(LBR)*	94	4842	6419	101,6	17,5	6,9	12	tk

Nordenhamer Chemikalien und Produkten Transport GmbH m.v. "Steersman" KG.

STEERSMAN *(LBR)*	94	4842	6404	101,6	17,5	6,9	12	tk

Chartered tonnage:

Linnea Shipping A/S

LINNEA *(NIS)*	80	6972	11520	149,5	19,5	6,7	13	tk
(ex Hydro-98)									

The company is a wholly owned subsidiary of JAMES FISHER & SONS Public Limited Company*qv*
Note: Management of the fleet is undertaken by JAMES FISHER & SONS (LIVERPOOL) *qv*

KG FISSER & v. DOORNUM GmbH & CO.

Feldbrunnenstrasse 43-45, 20148 Hamburg, Germany (+49 040 44186241/fax +49 040 445686)
Agents only for:

Tealbay Shipping Co Ltd

CORONA *(CYP)*	98	4095	4800	100,0	16,2	6,4	14	gen(374c)

Kinsale Shipping Co Ltd

KENMARE *(CYP)*	75	5306	8110	117,6	18,1	7,2	14	bulk
(ex Raute-86, Singapura-83, Raute-78)									
KINSALE *(CYP)*	76	5306	8150	117,6	18,1	7,3	15	bulk(170c)
(ex Rhombus-86, Wachau-84, Bayu-83, Rhombus-78)									

FORTHLINE LTD.
Earl Building, Central Dock Road, Carron Dock, Grangemouth, Lothian, FK3 8TY
(01324 664409/fax 01324 665018)
Chartered tonnage.:

m.s. "Canopus" Rohden Schiffahrts GmbH & Co KG

CANOPUS I (CYP)	79	2862	2507	98,7	16,0	3,8	12	gen(204c)
(ex Canopus-94)								

Phoenix Reederei GmbH m.s. "Sirius P" KG

HIGHLAND (ATG)	90	2440	3181	87,5	13,0	4,8	12	gen(153c)
(ex Sirrah-95)								

Note: FORTHLINE is a wholly owned subsidiary of Forth Ports PLC.

FRODSHAM LIGHTERAGE CO.
9 Poulton Green Close, Spital, Bebington, Wirral, L63 9FC (0151 334 6715/fax 0151 334 6715)

Humber & Hull River Lighterage

HULL PARAGON (GBR)	56	213	330	47,0	5,5	2,6	7	ed oil bge
(ex David W-96)								

Viaduct Shipping

PANARY (GBR)	37	167	260	29,5	6,5	2,6	8	gen bge

Managers for:

Logantor Ltd trading as Mersey Tanker Lighterage

SAFE HAND (GBR)	50	205	203	30,6	7,0	2,4	8	tk bge
(ex Lux-75)								

PHILIP FUCHTER trading as P. J. MARINE
10 Upberry Way, Chatham, ME4 4NQ (01634 829026/0973 624 123)

ROINA (GBR)	66	172	264	29,4	6,8	2,5	7	gen bge

GAELIC SEAFOODS (IRELAND) LTD.
Dernish Island, Castletownbere, Co Cork, Irish Republic (+353 27 70376)

WILBERNIA	60	93	120	24,5	5,0	1,5	8	gen bge
(ex Cowes-72)								

J. & A. GARDNER & CO LTD.
16 Robertson Street, Glasgow, G2 8DU (0141 221-7845/fax 0141 204-2388)

SAINT BRANDAN (GBR)	76	1017	1394	63,8	10,8	4,1	10	gen/ro
SAINT KEARAN (GBR)	78	439	775	50,4	9,1	3,3	9	ch tk
SAINT ORAN (GBR)	81	621	719	53,3	9,2	3,4	10	gen/ro/ch

Managers for:

Knapdale Shipping (Campbeltown) Ltd (Lithgows Ltd/J & A Gardner & Co Ltd)

CREAR (GBR)	97	381	440	34,6	8,6	4,0	9	fish

GENCHEM MARINE LTD.
Maritime House, 19A St Helens Street, Ipswich, Suffolk, IP4 1HE (01473 231121/fax 01473 232265)
Managers/agents for:

Parkside Warehousing & Transport

BORELLY (GBR)	71	571	905	55,7	9,9	3,3	10	gen
(ex Jana Weston-84)								

Whiting (Shipping) Ltd

BRENDONIAN (GBR)	66	587	837	54,0	9,1	3,6	10	gen
(ex Brendonia-84)								

Tara Shipping Ltd

ELLEN W (VCT)	74	459	645	47,8	8,8	3,1	9	gen
(ex Guy Chipperfield-82)								

GEORGE GIBSON & CO LTD.

11 John's Place, Leith, Edinburgh, EH6 7EL (0131 554-4466/fax 0131 554-3843)
Managers for:

Gibson Gas Tankers Ltd

EILDON *(LBR)*	82	6808	6920	114,4	18,3	7,6	14	lpg
(ex Norgas Transporter-98, Etienne Schlumberger-89)								
QUENTIN *(LBR)*	77	1709	2072	76,1	12,4	5,4	12	lpg
(ex Pentland Moor-79)								
YARROW *(CYM)*	82	6356	7850	115,1	18,5	8,5	14	lpg
(ex Norgas Mariner-98, Sigurd Jorsalfar-88, Nopal Norte-87)								
Lloyds Machinery Leasing Ltd								
ETTRICK *(LBR)*	91	3023	3621	88,0	14,9	6,0	14	lpg
Lanrick Gas (Private) Ltd								
LANRICK *(LBR)*	92	3023	3621	88,0	14,9	6,0	14	lpg
Gas Shipping & Transport (Jersey) Ltd								
TRAQUAIR *(LBR)*	82	5992	7230	113,8	18,4	8,1	16	lpg

*George Gibson's lpg tanker **ETTRICK** heads up the New Waterway on 7 July 1995.*   *(Jan van der Klooster)*

G. T. GILLIE & BLAIR LTD.

178 New Bridge Street, Newcastle upon Tyne, NE1 2TE (0191 232-3431/fax 0191 232-8255)
Managers for:

Ensign Express Shipping Ltd

RIVER DART *(GBR)*	81	536	825	50,0	9,3	3,4	10	gen

Note. Gillie & Blair *are commercial managers for other dry cargo vessels*

T. E. GRACE (West Country Sand & Gravel)

Rolle Quay, Barnstaple, N. Devon EX32 8JE (01271 45842/fax 01271 831029)

TED GRACE *(GBR)* *	49	113	202	30,6	5,4	2,4	8	sd
(ex Sand Pearl-80, Wycliffe-70)								
TERRY GRACE *(GBR)* *	33	158	200	30,6	6,6	2,4	7	gen bge
(ex Deerhurst-97)								
MARLENE GRACE *(GBR)*	66	62	76	18,3	5,5	2,3	11	sand
(ex Pen . . , Marley)								

West Country Sand & Gravel

BUSY GRACE *(GBR)* *	63	50	60	15,8	3,7	1,5	8	sand
(ex Busy Bee-89)								
LOUISA GRACE *(GBR)*	60	50	65	15,8	4,8	1,9	8	sand
(ex RH 13-79)								

*Note. : * Laid up Barnstaple*

GRACECHURCH CONTAINER LINE

2nd Floor, Port of Liverpool Buildings, Pier Head, Liverpool, L21 1BZ
(0151 231-1144/fax 0151 231 1375)
Chartered tonnage:
  Hermann Buss KG m.s. "Northsea Trader" GmbH & Co
GRACECHURCH

COMET *(ATG)*	95	4984	6954	116,4	19,5	7,1	16	cc(532c)

  (ex Northsea Trader-97, Texel Bay-96, Northsea Trader-95)
  Tom Worden Schiffahrtskontor GmbH
GRACECHURCH

METEOR *(DEU)*	97	3999	5500	100,0	18,2	6,6	16	cc(523c)

  (launched as Merino)
  Reederei m.s. "Gerdia" Heinz Freese K.G.

GRACECHURCH STAR *(ATG)*	94	5026	6450	117,0	18,2	6,9	16	gen(538c)

  (ex Gerdia-96, Alum Bay-96, Gerdia-94)
  Schiffahrtsges m.s. "Uranus" Heinz Corleis KG ??

GRACECHURCH SUN *(DEU)*	92	5006	6449	116,7	18,2	6,9	16	gen(510c)

  (ex Uranus-97)
  Partenreederei m.s. "Katherine Borchard"
KATHERINE

BORCHARD *(ATG)*	79	5378	7198	126,3	18,1	6,5	15	gen(462c)

  (ex Concordia-86, Katherine Borchard-86, Concordia-85, Zim Australia-82, launched as Concordia)
The company is a wholly owned subsidiary of BORCHARD LINES LTD *qv*

EDMUND HALM & CO. GmbH.

Feldbrunnenstrasse 43-45, Postfach 132265, 20148 Hamburg, Germany (+49 040 44186241/fax +49
040 44186211)
Agents only for:
  Alsace Shipping Co Ltd

KELLS *(CYP)*	77	1986	2657	79,2	12,4	4,7	10	gen(104c)

  (ex Gotaland-88)
Managers for:
  Emerald Isle Bulkers Ltd

KILLARNEY *(IRL)*	77	2563	2908	96,3	12,4	4,8	12	gen(207c)

  (ex Anholt-86, Neuwerk-81)

KYLEMORE *(IRL)*	77	2563	2908	96,3	12,4	4,7	12	gen(207c)

  (ex Borssum-95, Bregenz-92, Bornholm-86, Neukloster-81)

HAY & CO (LERWICK) LTD.

66 Commercial Road, Lerwick, Shetland, ZE1 0NJ (01595 692533/fax 01595 692781)
Managers for:
  John Fleming & Co (Holdings) Ltd

SHETLAND TRADER *(GBR)*	80	909	1315	60,0	11,3	3,9	12	gen

  (ex Portland-97, Comity-94, Angelonia-88)

HENTY OIL LTD.
No.1 Huskisson Dock, Liverpool,L3 0AT (0151 922 0622/fax 0151 922 0626)
TAFFGARTH *(GBR)*   50   161   236   37,0   5,9   2,1   7   bk tk bge
(ex Contractor-85, Regent Wren-71)
WHEATCROFT *(GBR)*   57   189   300   42,8   5,5   2,1   7   bk tk bge

PETER M. HERBERT
Bideford, N. Devon
JOHN ADAMS *(GBR)*   34   94   165   26,0   6,0   2,8   7   gen
Note :   Laid up Bideford (East-the-Water)

TANKSKIBSREDERIET HERNING A/S (HERNING SHIPPING A/S)
Utzonhuset, Olufsvaenget 29, 7400 Herning, Denmark (+ 45 97126777/fax +45 97 127279)
Managers for:
I/S m.t. Grete Theresa II
GRETE THERESA *(IOM)*   68   772   1061   64,0   9,9   3,9   11   oil/ch tk
(ex Unicorn Michael-91, Onabi-77)

HIGHLAND CARRIER SHIPPING LTD.
41 Culduthel Road, Inverness, IV2 4AT (01463 223821/ fax 01463 220901)
HIGHLAND CARRIER *(BHS)*   81   1155   1266   64,0   14,5   3,7   11   ro(46c)
(ex Trinity Bay-98, Leichhardt-90)
Note: Managed by   INTRADA CHARTERING *qv*

HIGHLAND MARINE LTD.
Railway Pier, Kyle of Lochalsh, Ross-shire, IV40 8AL (01599 534820/fax 01599 534865)
Managers for:
Roderick Cunningham (Scalpay) Ltd
ISLE OF TIREE *(GBR)*   61   131   78   29,0   7,1   2,7   11   gen
(ex Ocean Hunter (A 197)-74, Caledonian (A 197)-71)
Bareboat charter:
Eidesvik Shipping (UK) Ltd
SALINA II *(PAN)*   62   212   371   35,4   7,5   3,2   9   gen
(ex Salina-97, Karla-92, Mebeto-71, Tommelise-65)

D V HOWELLS MARINE (DVH)
Milford Docks, Milford Haven, Pembrokeshire, SA73 3AF (01646 692418/ fax 01646 690179)
HELMSDALE *(GBR)*   55   110   200   26,9   5,9   2,1   7   bk tk bge
(ex Helmsdale H)
WIKNER *(GBR)*   50   87   110   21,1   6,6   2,1   6   gen
bge(cr)
(ex S.A. Wikner)

HUELIN-RENOUF SHIPPING SERVICES.
PO Box 17, New North Quay, St Helier, Jersey, CI (01534 610345/fax 01534 610346)
HUELIN DISPATCH *(BHS)*   78   1892   2360   79,8   12,8   4,5   12   gen(104c)
(ex Stenholm-96, Visbur-92, Stenholm-91, Suderelv-91)

HYDRO SEAFOOD GSP LTD.
South Shian, Connel, Oban, Argyll, PA37 1SB (01631 574000/fax 01631 720465)
SOLEA *(GBR)*   89   235   326   33,5   7,6   3,4   9   fish
Chartered tonnage:
Solv Trans A/S
RONJACHRISTOPHER *(NOR)* 97   499   650   40,4   10,0   4,2   9   fish

INTERNATIONAL CHARTERING PLC.

15 Gloster Road, Martlesham Heath, Ipswich, Suffolk, IP5 7RJ (01473 626646/fax 01473 610256)

SWIFT TRADER *(IOM)*	77	1899	2621	79,8	13,2	5,2	12	gen
(ex Swift-85)								

INTERNATIONAL SHIPBROKERS LTD.

7 Crescent, London EC3N 2LY (0171 680 0068/fax 0171 680 9702)

Managers for:

Partenreederei m.s. "Ahrenshoop"

AHRENSHOOP *(DEU)*	70	1641	1350	75,7	11,3	3,6	12	gen(74c)
(ex Frakto-78, Stokkfrakt-77, Frakto-75, Anglo Unit-74, Karen Oltmann-72)								

Reinhold Fischer KG

UTE *(DEU)*	84	1520	1837	76,5	11,5	3,9	10	gen

Time chartered tonnage:

Kapt. Andre Wieczorek

CLARA *(ATG)*	75	1672	2130	75,8	11,8	4,7	11	gen(82c)
(ex Anita-95, Heide-Catrin-91)								

Rederij Harma

HARMA *(NLD)*	79	999	1455	65,0	10,7	4,0	10	gen

Gunter Meyer

UNIKA *(ATG)*	71	1773	1426	76,6	12,8	4,1	12	gen(163c)
(ex Arnis-85)								

Note : International Shipbrokers *are also chartering managers/agents for vessels listed under other owners*

The **AHRENSHOOP** lies at Medina Wharf, Cowes, on 11 October 1998.   (Brian Ralfs)

INTERSEA OPERATIONS LTD INC.

PO Box 7560, 3000 HN Rotterdam, Netherlands (+31 0181 240 3403/fax +31 0181 355535)

Managers for:

Chesham Containerships Ltd

AMERSHAM *(GBR)*	80	6764	9663	120,8	20,9	7,9	14	cc(528c)
(ex Panarea I-96)								
CHESHAM *(GBR)*	80	6764	9809	120,8	20,9	7,9	14	cc(528c)
(ex Oahu-96)								
DENHAM *(GBR)*	80	6764	9809	120,8	20,9	7,9	15	cc(528c)
(ex La Trinity-97, Pagai-92)								

INTRADA CHARTERING LTD.
75 Main Road, Gidea Park, Romford, Essex , RM2 5EL (01708 739-353/fax 01708 739-252)
All vessels are on charter to Scotline Ltd.
Managers for:

Hohebank Shipping Ltd

HOHEBANK *(BHS)*	78	1687	1851	79,7	12,8	3,7	11	gen(82c)

Scot Pioneer Shipping Ltd

SCOT PIONEER *(BHS)*	84	1587	1901	82,2	11,5	4,2	10	gen
(ex Silvia-98)								

Scot Ranger Shipping Ltd

SCOT RANGER *(BHS)*	97	2250	3360	84,9	12,6	5,1	11	gen

Scot Trader Shipping Ltd

SCOT TRADER *(BHS)*	86	1584	1900	82,0	11,5	4,2	10	gen
(ex Wotan-93, Scot Trader-91, Wotan-86)								

Chartered tonnage:

Wolfgang & Carsten Kleige

CHARLOTTE *(ATG)*	69	1440	1477	77,2	11,8	4,0	11	gen(72c)
(ex Hinrich Behrmann-89, Tweed-70, launched as Hinrich Behrmann)								

Heinz Litmeyer Schiffahrts K.G. m.s. "Emsland"

EMSLAND *(ATG)*	84	1857	2200	80,2	12,7	4,2	11	gen(102c)

Jan Peter Ludtke KG

INGA *(DEU)*	85	1584	1783	82,0	11,5	3,5	10	gen

Partenreederei m.s. "Konigsburg"

KORALLE *(ATG)*	85	1851	2269	80,0	12,7	4,2	10	gen(142c)
(ex RMS Hollandia-94, Koralle-92)								

*The **SCOT TRADER** passes Chatham on her way down the River Medway on 8 September 1997 after discharging a cargo of timber at Rochester.* *(Peter Hutchison)*

ISLE OF MAN STEAM PACKET CO. LTD.
Imperial Buildings, PO Box 5, Bath Place, Douglas, IoM, IM99 1AF
(01624 645620/fax01624 645609)

BEN-MY-CHREE *(IOM)*	98	3800	2200	125,2	23,4	5,0	19	ro/px(93u/200a)
PEVERIL *(IOM)* *	71	5254	1685	106,3	16,0	5,0	14	ro(45u)
(ex N. F. Jaguar-82, Penda-80, ASD Meteor-75, Holmia-73)								

Note : * Laid up Birkenhead

ISLES OF SCILLY STEAMSHIP CO. LTD.

Hugh Town, St Mary's, PO Box 10, Isles of Scilly (01720 422357/fax 01720 422192) & Quay Street,
Penzance, TR18 4BD (01736 62009 /fax 01736 51223)

GRY MARITHA *(GBR)*	81	590	528	40,3	9,8	3,7	9	gen/pt

R. LAPTHORN & CO. LTD.

Buttercrock Wharf, Vicarage Lane, Hoo, Rochester, Kent, ME3 9LQ
(01634   250369/fax 01634 250759)

ANNA MERYL *(GBR)*	91	999	1704	69,1	9,9	3,9	9	gen
(ex Anna Maria-94)								
HOO VENTURE *(GBR)*	82	671	1230	50,0	9,5	4,0	8	gen
HOOCREEK *(GBR)*	82	671	1236	50,0	9,4	4,1	8	gen

Managers for:

John H. Whitaker (Holdings) Ltd

ANTONIA B *(GBR)*	83	671	1230	50,0	9,5	4,0	9	gen
(ex Whitonia-97)								

John H. Whitaker (Holdings) Ltd & Bayford & Co Ltd

BETTY-JEAN *(GBR)*	85	794	1360	58,3	9,5	3,9	8	gen
FAST KEN *(GBR)*	92	1382	2220	77,8	11,1	4,0	9	gen
(ex Bowcliffe-94)								

R. Lapthorn Shipping Ltd

HOO BEECH *(GBR)*	89	794	1399	58,3	9,5	3,6	9	gen
HOO DOLPHIN *(GBR)*	86	794	1412	58,3	9,6	3,9	9	gen
HOO LARCH *(GBR)*	92	1382	2225	77,8	11,1	4,0	10	gen
HOO LAUREL *(GBR)*	84	794	1394	58,3	9,5	3,9	8	gen
HOO MAPLE *(GBR)*	89	794	1399	58,3	9,5	3,9	9	gen
HOO MARLIN *(GBR)*	86	794	1412	58,3	9,5	3,9	8	gen
HOO PLOVER *(GBR)*	83	671	1234	50,0	9,5	4,0	8	gen
HOO ROBIN *(GBR)*	89	794	1399	58,3	9,5	3,9	9	gen
HOO TERN *(GBR)*	85	794	1394	58,3	9,5	3,9	8	gen
HOO WILLOW *(GBR)*	84	671	1234	50,0	9,5	4,0	8	gen
HOOCREST *(GBR)*	86	794	1400	58,3	9,6	3,9	9	gen
HOOPRIDE *(GBR)*	84	794	1394	58,3	9,5	3,9	8	gen

*The **HOOCREST** passes Northfleet as she leaves the River Thames on 24 January 1998.*   (Kevin Bassett)

R. Lapthorn & Co Ltd & R. Lapthorn Shipping Ltd

HOO FALCON *(GBR)*	91	1382	2225	77,8	11,1	4,0	9	gen
HOO FINCH *(GBR)*	89	794	1377	58,3	9,5	3,9	9	gen
HOO KESTREL *(GBR)*	93	1382	2225	77,8	11,1	4,0	10	gen
HOO SWAN *(GBR)*	86	794	1412	58,3	9,5	3,9	8	gen
HOO SWIFT *(GBR)*	89	794	1399	58,3	9,5	3,9	9	gen

Harris & Dixon (Shipbrokers) Ltd

ILONA G *(GBR)*	90	999	1700	69,1	10,8	3,9	10	gen

Waveney Shipping II PLC

NICKY L *(GBR)*	76	1220	1897	78,4	10,8	4,1	11	gen

(ex Magrix-98, The Dutch-87, Tanja Holwerda-87, Roelof Holwerda-81)

FREDERICK CHARLES LARKHAM & SONS LTD.

Severn Mill, The Strand, Westbury-on-Severn, Glos, GL14 1PG (01452 760368/fax 01452 760368)

BACCARAT *(GBR)*	59	293	325	45,7	8,7	2,2	8	tk bge/gen
BOXER *(GBR)*	65	197	315	35,1	7,6	2,0	8	gen bge
HOOK SAND *(GBR)* +	64	186	280	35,4	7,2	2,7	7	sd

(ex Polo III-81, Amanda-75)

Note : + Operated by Forrest Sands, Chepstow; *also engaged in maintenance dredging if required*

LEAFE & HAWKES LTD.

Merrick Street, Hedon Road, Hull, HU9 1NF (01482 325951/fax 01482 225406)
Managers for:

Hammann & Prahm Reedereiges mbH & Co. KG m.s. "Eric Hammann"

ERIC HAMMANN *(DEU)*	91	1156	1323	58,8	11,7	3,6	9	gen(50c)

Reederei Hammann & Prahm GmbH & Co KG m.s. "Evert Prahm"

EVERT PRAHM *(DEU)*	96	1598	2390	76,4	12,7	4,5	10	gen

Hammann & Prahm Bereederungsges mbH & Co KG m.s. "Gerhard Prahm"

GERHARD PRAHM *(DEU)*	82	1022	1089	74,5	9,5	2,9	10	gen

(ex RMS Bavaria-96, Gerhard Prahm-92)

Hammann & Prahm GmbH & Co.KG

LORE PRAHM *(DEU)*	89	1156	1323	58,0	11,8	3,6	9	gen(50c)
WALTER HAMMANN *(DEU)*	88	1156	1323	58,8	11,7	3,5	9	gen(50c)

*The **EVERT PRAHM** cautiously approaches the port of Leer in Germany.*   *(Ron Wood)*

Hammann & Prahm Bereererungsges mbH & Co KG m.s. "Martha Hammann"
MARTHA HAMMANN *(DEU)* 85 1832 2287 80,7 12,7 4,2 11 gen(112c)
Reederei Hammann & Prahm GmbH & Co KG m.s. "Rebecca Hammann"
REBECCA HAMMANN *(DEU)* 95 1595 2350 76,4 12,7 4,5 10 gen
Hammann & Prahm Reedereiges mbH & Co. m.s. "Selene Prahm"
SELENE PRAHM *(DEU)* 94 1584 2422 75,1 12,7 4,5 10 gen
Hammann & Prahm Bereederungsges mbH & Co KG m.s "Sheila Hammann"
SHEILA HAMMANN *(DEU)* 83 1022 1113 74,5 9,5 2,9 10 gen
(ex RMS Anglia-96, Sheila Hammann-92)
m.s. "Wilhelmine Steffens" Reederei Steffens GmbH & Co
WILHELMINE
STEFFENS *(DEU)* 81 1022 1092 74,3 9,5 2,9 10 gen
(ex RMS Scotia-96, Wilhelmine Steffens-92, Lucky Star-91)

LIBRA SHIPPING B.V.
Maaskade 159A, 3071 NR Rotterdam, Netherlands (+31 010 4117740/fax +31 010 4117769)
Agents only for:
Primula Ltd
BLACKBIRD *(VCT)* 67 1197 1735 75,8 11,2 4,4 12 gen
(ex Hawthorn-92, Francinaplein-77, Hunnau-73, Ortrud Muller-69)
Regulus Ltd
BLUEBIRD *(VCT)* 82 1115 1688 67,4 11,3 4,1 10 gen(54c)
(ex Alice-95, Alila-92, Peacock Venture-88)
Cormorant Shipping & Trading Ltd
EGRET *(VCT)* 66 633 738 57,4 9,1 2,8 9 gen
(ex Cormorant-86, Moon Trader-86, A. Held-79)

*The **EGRET** gets under way in Belfast's Herdman Channel on 13 May 1994.*   *(Alan Geddes)*

LINCOLN & HULL MARINE CONTRACTORS LTD.
100 Lime Street, Hull, HU8 7AR (01482 320727/fax 01482 320727)
PANURGIC *(GBR)* 50 139 120 33,8 7,3 2,5 8 gen
bge(cr)
Managers for:
D.J. & G. & K. Hornshaw
LANEHAM *(GBR)* 65 217 400 44,5 6,6 2,5 8 gen bge

HOT River Traders

MARNHAM *(GBR)*	68	250	450	44,5	7,0	2,5	8	gen bge
Hughes Marine								
NORMANTON *(GBR)*	68	231	400	44,5	6,6	2,5	8	gen bge
SWINDERBY *(GBR)*	74	340	550	46,0	8,6	3,0	8	gen bge(cr)
TORKSEY *(GBR)*	69	250	450	44,5	7,0	2,5	8	gen bge

LLANELLI SAND DREDGING LTD.
Windmill Park, Burry Port, Dyfed (01554 832475)
Chartered tonnage:
Baggermaatschappij Boskalis B.V.

SOSPAN *(PAN)* +	90	718	1300	57,0	10,0	3,6	7	drg/hpr

Note : + Also employed on maintenance & capital dredging in EU waters. The company is part of the Royal Boskalis Westminster Group

LOTHIAN SHIPPING SERVICES (LONDON) LTD.
53-55 High Street, Ruislip, Middlesex, HA4 7AZ (01895 676341/fax 01895 675729)
Managers for:
Powergen Plc

LORD CITRINE *(GBR)*	86	14201	22447	154,9	24,5	9,0	12	bulk
LORD HINTON *(GBR)*	86	14201	22447	154,9	24,5	9,0	12	bulk
SIR CHARLES								
PARSONS *(GBR)*	85	14201	22530	154,9	24,5	9,0	12	bulk

The company is a wholly owned subsidiary of Unicom Management Services (Cyprus) Ltd *the shipmanagement arm of* AKP Sovcomflot, Moscow

*The **LORD HINTON** approaches the Tyne Coal Terminal to load a cargo on 3 April 1995.* *(Barry Standerline)*

MAERSK CO. (I.O.M.) LTD.
Portland House, Station Road, Ballasalla, Isle of Man (01624 822667/fax 01624 822618)
Managers for:
Oxgate Security Co Ltd

MAERSK ANGLIA *(IOM)*	77	6862	3526	122,9	21,0	4,8	15	ro(90u)

(ex Duke of Anglia-90, Saint Remy-86, Admiral Caribe-82, Admiral Nigeria-79, Admiral Caribe-77)
Note: Vessel is operating on The Ford Motor Co Ltd, Dagenham, *contract*

*Mezeron's **SILVER RIVER** was photographed leaving Belfast via the Herdman Channel on 29 May 1997.*
(Alan Geddes)

*Also viewed from a high vantage point - the Humber Bridge - are the barges **NORMANTON** (nearer the camera) and **TORKSEY**. Both were heading for the River Trent on 22 February 1998.* *(Richard Potter)*

*In bright autumn sunlight, the **HOPE** approaches Cowes, Isle of Wight, on 14 November 1997.*

(Brian Ralfs)

*After discharging a cargo of bulk cement, Crescent Shipping's **KINDRENCE** approaches the lock at Swansea prior to sailing up the Bristol Channel to Sharpness on 18 August 1997.*   *(Bill Moore, courtesy ABP Swansea)*

The **CELTIC NAVIGATOR** is about to depart from Swansea on 9 April 1996. She is heading for Portugal with a cargo of steel coils. *(Bill Moore, courtesy ABP Swansea)*

Tankers operated by the Whitaker group of companies can be found in several estuaries. The **WHITASK** is one of the vessels based on the Solent. *(Brian Ralfs)*

*F T Everard's **SAGACITY** loads stone at Llysfaen Jetty, Llanddulas, on 16 July 1998.*   *(John P Evans)*

*The industrial and residential suburbs of Le Havre form the backdrop to this photograph of the **YVETTE** as she loads containers on 13 December 1997.*   *(Bernard McCall)*

MASOUMA SHIPPING LINES

31/33 Station Road, Hendon, London, NW4 4PN, (0181 2024366/fax 0181 2024601)
Managers for:

Masouma Investments Ltd

AL MASOOMA *(BLZ)*	66	1261	1972	73,0	11,3	5,0	12	gen

(ex Craigmore-96, Stavroula-91, Avra Z-89, Craigmore-87)

McKENNA MARINE SERVICES LTD.

343 Sutton Park, Sutton, Dublin 13, Irish Republic (+ 353 1 8326745/fax +353 1 8321769)
Managers for:

Ominar Shipping Co Ltd

FIONA MAY *(CYP)*	77	999	1632	61,5	10,4	4,8	9	gen

(ex Serenell-95)

MEDWAY SHIPPING LTD.

"Roseville", Danes Hill, Gillingham, Kent, ME7 2TU(01634 851177/fax 01634 581213)

CECIL GILDERS *(GBR)*	57	137	224	27,7	6,5	2,4	7	gen bge

MERCHANT FERRIES LTD.

North Quay, Heysham Harbour, Morecambe, Lancashire, LA3 2UL
(01524 855018/fax 01524 852527)

Proofbrand Ltd

MERCHANT BRAVERY *(BHS)*	78	9368	5290	134,8	21,7	5,0	17	ro(90u)

(ex Jolly Giallo-93, Norwegian Crusader-82, Jolly Giallo-82, Norwegian Crusader-80, launched as Stevi)

MERCHANT BRILLIANT *(BHS)*	79	9368	5300	133,1	21,7	5,0	17	ro(90u)

(ex Jolly Bruno-93, Norwegian Challenger-82)

MERCHANT VENTURE *(IOM)*	79	6056	3671	119,4	19,5	5,2	17	ro(50u/169c)

(ex Merchant Isle-87, Argentea-87, Med Adriatico-85, Farman-82)

Note : The company is a wholly owned subsidiary of Cenargo Ltd. Vessels are managed by V SHIPS (UK) qv

MERMAID MARINE MANAGEMENT LTD.

Hoopers Hill House, Angel Lane, Lymington Road, New Milton, Hants, BH25 5PZ
(01425 619262/fax 01425 619237)
Managers for:

Delship Corp

ALPINE GIRL *(BHS)*	75	3984	6418	110,0	16,6	6,9	14	ch tk

(ex Dintel-86, Quimico Lisboa-86, launched as Chemist Lisbon)

Delship Trading Corp

ALPINE LADY *(BHS)*	77	4009	6433	110,5	16,6	6,9	14	ch tk

(ex Multitank Antares-88, Dommel-87, Quimico Leixoes-86)

MERSEY SAND SUPPLIERS LTD.

East Side Trafalgar Dock, Liverpool, L3 0AG (0151 236 6646/fax 0151 236 4184)
Operators for:

Norwest Sand & Ballast Co Ltd

NORSTAR *(GBR)*	61	614	1125	47,6	11,0	4,2	9	sd

MEZERON LTD.

East Quay, Ramsey, IoM, IM8 1BG (01624 812302/fax 01624 815613)

AULDYN RIVER *(IOM)*	61	417	650	54,2	7,6	2,3	8	gen

(ex Claudia W-97, Eberstein-79)

SILVER RIVER *(IOM)*	68	277	373	44,7	7,4	2,7	10	gen

(ex Nathurn-86, Sea Trent-82, Seacon-71)

MILFORD HAVEN PORT AUTHORITY.

Port of Pembroke, Pembroke Dock, Dyfed, SA72 6TD   (01646 683981/fax 01646 687394)

G . D. DISTRIBUTOR *(GBR)*	74	589	693	59,1	10,0	2,5	10	bk tk bge
(ex Shell Distributor-91, Harty-79)								

Note : Laid up Pembroke Dock.

MORLINE LTD.

Morline House, London Road, Barking, Essex, IG11 8BB (0181 507 6099/fax 0181 507 6090)

Managers for:

Beacon 2 Shipping Co Ltd

BEACON 2 *(MLT)*	73	2317	1423	80,5	12,8	4,2	13	ro(13u/128c)

(ex Manilaid-96, Thunar-75)

Island Navigation Co Ltd

BEACON 3 *(MLT)*	75	7156	6447	129,4	19,2	7,5	17	cc(304c)

(ex Aleksandr Prokofyev-96)

A/O Sovfracht

INZHENER *(RUS)*	74	8301	6128	124,2	19,6	7,0	16	ro(239c)

(ex Inzhener Machulsky-96)

Bennav Shipping Co Ltd

LEO *(MLT)*	73	1597	2987	87,5	12,0	5,5	12	gen

(ex Adriatic-88, Moidart-86)

Northern Shipping Co

MEKHANIK

ZHELTOVSKIY *(RUS)*	80	5634	5720	130,0	17,4	6,9	15	cc(320c)

Bulkway Shipping Ltd

VITA *(MLT)*	69	2723	3950	102,3	14,0	6,2	13	gen

(ex Kaliningrad-96)

NORD SHIP MANAGEMENT LTD.

Garthspool, Lerwick, Shetland Islands, ZE1 0NP (01595 692556/fax01595 695949)

CELEBRITY *(GBR)* +	76	633	946	57,6	10,0	3,3	10	gen
NORDSTAR *(GBR)*	78	460	727	49,3	9,0	3,2	10	gen

(ex Kava Sound-94, Ordinence-89)

Managers for:

HVC Ltd

COMMODITY *(GBR)* +	75	633	946	57,6	10,0	3,3	10	gen

Note : + Freight managers F. T. Everard & Sons Management Ltd *qv*

*The **NORD STAR** passes Newburgh on the River Tay on 28 June 1995.*   *(Richard Jones)*

NORDTANK SHIPPING ApS.

Lindevej 16, 4300 Holbaek, Denmark (+45 59 44 44 66/fax +45 59 44 44 60)
Managers for:

Uni-Tankers

BALTIC SWAN	(IOM)	68	2615	4924	105,2	12,6	6,4	12	tk
(ex Furetank-97, Tarntank-84)									
Uni-Tankers m.t."Haahr Bridge"									
HAAHR BRIDGE	(IOM)	67	1131	2104	74,6	10,2	4,9	11	tk
(ex Brevik-95, launched as Venern)									
Uni-tankers m.t. "Haahr Trumf"									
HAAHR TRUMF	(IOM)	64	1133	1946	74,4	10,2	4,9	12	tk
(ex Candy I-95, Candy-90, Arholma-85, Smaragd-80, Sibell-79, Cortina-77, Tarnsjo-70)									

NORFOLK LINE B.V.

Kranenburgweg 211, Scheveningen, 2583 ER 's Gravenhage, The Netherlands
(+31 70 3527402/fax+31 70 3545579)
and **NORFOLK LINE LTD**, Norfolk House, The Dock, Felixstowe, Suffolk, IP11 8UY
(01394 603713/fax 01394 603680)
Managers for:

Norfolk Scheepvaartmaatschappij B.V.

MAERSK EXPORTER	(NLD)	96	13017	5928	142,4	23,3	5,4	18	ro(120u)
MAERSK FLANDERS	(NLD)	78	7199	3523	122,9	21,0	4,8	16	ro(90u)
(ex Duke of Flanders-90, Romira-86, Admiral Atlantic-84)									
MAERSK IMPORTER	(NLD)	96	13017	5928	142,4	23,3	5,4	18	ro(120u)
New buildings (2)(Guangzhou Shipyard, China)									
	mid	99	13000	5900	142,4	23,3	5,4	18	ro(120u)
	Jan	00	13000	5900	142,4	23,3	5,4	18	ro(120u)

Chartered tonnage:

Octogon Shipping & Services

BOLERO	(ROM)	85	10243	6704	141,0	23,5	6,5	14	ro(65u)
(ex Tuzla-96, launched as Spiegelberg)									

Chartered tonnage (Waterford-Rotterdam service):

Partenreederei m.s. "Jan Becker" Bernd Becker KG

JAN BECKER	(DEU)	87	2749	3173	94,5	16,2	5,0	14	gen(262c)
Partenreederei m.s. "Otto Becker"									
OTTO BECKER	(DEU)	89	2749	3144	94,5	16,1	5,0	14	gen(262c)

The companies are part of the A. P. Moller/Maersk Group

NORSE MANAGEMENT (U.K.) LTD.

Copford Hall, Copford, Colchester, Essex, CO6 1DG (01206 212001/fax 01206 212552)
Time chartered tonnage:

Levantina Trasporti S.r.l.

LAGAN VIKING	(ITA)	97	21856	1500	186,0	26,0	5,6	24	ro/px(164u/100a)
Francesco Visentini Transport Fluvio Marittimi									
MERSEY VIKING	(ITA)	97	21856	1500	186,0	26,0	5,6	24	ro/px(164u/100a)

NORTECH (SCOTLAND) LTD.

70 Northburn Road, Coatbridge, Lanarkshire, ML5 2HY (01236 427514/fax 01236 441148)

FULFORD	(GBR)	60	477	522	50,3	10,2	2,6	10	tk
(ex Charmo-91)									
PERFECTO	(GBR)	67	652	1008	59,2	10,7	3,2	9	tk
(ex Shell Driver-89, Perfecto-79)									

NORTH AFRICA MIDDLE EAST SHIPPING & ENGINEERING CO. HOLLAND B.V. (NAMESECO HOLLAND B.V.)

Westplein 5, 3016 BM Rotterdam, The Netherlands (+31 010 4367299/fax +31 010 4369016)
Managers for:
(Nowal Ltd) S.W. Shipping Ltd

S W RUNNER *(IOM)*	65	575	762	62,3	9,5	3,1	10	ch tk

(ex Goldcrest-98, Silverkestrel-94, Goldcrest-92, Carrick Kestrel-87, Silverkestrel-75)

S W TRADER *(GBR)*	66	688	952	57,0	9,8	4,4	11	ch tk

(ex Sandlark-98, Silverlark-94, Sandlark-92, Ice Lark-87, Finnlark-76)

NORTH WEST WATER LTD.

Dawson House, Warrington, Cheshire, WA5 3LW (01925 724321)

CONSORTIUM I *(GBR)*	72	2384	3623	91,0	14,2	5,4	13	sludge
GILBERT J. FOWLER *(GBR)* *	71	2384	3623	91,0	14,2	5,4	13	sludge

*Note : * Laid up Liverpool*

NORTHERN MARINE MANAGEMENT LTD.

Alba House, 2 Central Avenue, Clydebank Business Park, Clydebank, Dunbartonshire, G81 2QR
(0141 9526844/fax 0141 94112791)
Managers for:
Stena Florida Line Ltd

STENA SHIPPER *(BHS)*	79	12337	8765	168,8	20,2	6,5	17	ro(150u)

(ex Nestor-94, Caribbean Stream-91, Nestor-90, African Gateway-89, Nestor-87, Nestor 1-85, Nestor-84)
Note : Chartered to COBELFRET, see EUROSHIP SERVICES. See also STENA LINE

NORTHWOOD (FAREHAM) LTD.

Westminster House, Crompton Way, Segensworth West, Fareham, Hants, PO15 5SS
(01329 235717/fax 01329 822697)

NORLEADER *(GBR)*	67	1592	2420	78,1	13,8	4,7	12	sd
NORSTONE *(GBR)*	71	1143	1803	67,2	12,5	4,5	10	sd

(ex Sand Skua-97)

WIGHTSTONE *(GBR)*	67	439	655	52,7	8,3	3,0	9	sand

(ex Michael Ane-97, Sanmark-95, Ilen-93, Patmarie-89, Sanmar-87, Union Sun-84, Andre-74)
Managers for:
Cortend Ltd

DONALD REDFORD *(GBR)*	81	681	964	53,5	10,7	3,4	9	sd

The **DONALD REDFORD** brings a cargo of sand up Southampton Water on 26 October 1998.

(Tony Atkinson)

NWS EUROPE LTD.

First Floor, New Hibernia House, Winchester Walk, London, SE1 9AG
(0171 403 9779/fax 0171 403 5677)
Agents only for:

Ob-Irtysh River Shipping Co (Ob-Irtyshskoye Rechnoye Parokhodstvo)

ISHIM *(RUS)*	78	1522	1755	81,9	11,9	3,4	9	gen
PUR *(RUS)*	79	1522	1755	82,0	11,8	3,4	9	gen (70c)

Sibir Shipping Co Ltd

SIBIR *(KHM)*	74	507	711	42,5	10,0	4,2	9	gen

(ex Seacombe Trader-98)

"Sibnec' Shareholders Association Ltd

SIBNEC *(RUS)*	65	1948	2624	96,0	13,2	3,8	10	gen

(ex Baltiyskiy 27-96)

ORCARGO LTD.

Norlantic House,10A Junction Road, Kirkwall, Orkney, KW15 1LB
(01856 873838/fax 01856 876521)

CONTENDER *(GBR)*	73	2292	1357	79,0	13,3	4,2	15	ro/gen(12u)

(ex Indiana I-92, Indiana-88, Ferruccio-86, Antinea-83)

ORKNEY LINE

Hatstone Industrial Estate, Kirkwall, Orkney IslandsKW15 1ER (01856 873658/fax 01856 873563)
and
SHETLAND LINE

Garthspool, Lerwick, Shetland Islands, ZE1 0NP (01595 692869/fax 01595 692234)
Chartered tonnage:

North Transit Marine Inc

BALTIC CHAMP *(PAN)*	77	1660	2060	72,0	12,8	4,5	12	gen(132c)

(ex Pico Ruivo-95, Nordlicht II-83)

*The **BALTIC CHAMP** maintains a regular service linking Aberdeen to Lerwick and Kirkwall. This aerial view
was taken as she made her way through the North Sea on 27 September 1996.* *(Richard Jones)*

P&O FERRYMASTERS LTD.

PO Box Southbank 12, Teesport, Grangetown, Middlesbrough, TS6 7RZ
(01642 394600/fax 01642 394666)
Managers for:

West Merchant Bank Ltd, BNP Leasing Ltd, C.T.S.B. Leasing Ltd & A.E.B.(UK)Ltd

ELK *(GBR)*	77	14374	9700	163,6	21,7	7,3	18	ro(130u)

Chartered tonnage:

Levantina Trasporti S.r.l.

NORSE MERSEY *(ITA)*	95	16009	11000	174,5	24,4	6,5	19	ro(125u)

P&O SHIP MANAGEMENT (IRISH SEA) LTD.

Copse Road, Fleetwood, Lancs, FY7 6HR (01253 615841/fax 01253 615849)
Managers & Operators for:

Abbey National March Leasing (1) Ltd

EUROPEAN ENDEAVOUR *(BMU)*	78	8097	3767	117,9	20,3	5,1	18	ro(76u)

(ex European Enterprise-88)

EUROPEAN TRADER *(BMU)*	75	8007	3953	117,9	20,3	5,8	18	ro(76u)

Pandoro Ltd

EUROPEAN ENVOY *(BMU)*	79	18653	4267	150,0	24,4	5,1	19	ro(133u)

(ex Ibex-97, Norsky-95, Norsea-86, Ibex-80)

EUROPEAN LEADER *(BMU)*	75	10987	4377	157,0	19,6	5,8	18	ro(100u)

(ex Buffalo-98)

EUROPEAN NAVIGATOR *(BMU)*	77	9085	3775	137,3	18,1	5,7	18	ro(70u)

(ex Leopard-98, Viking Trader-96, Oyster Bay-83, Manaure VII-83, Caribbean Sky-81, Federal Nova-81, Goya-79, launched as Stena Tender)

EUROPEAN PATHFINDER *(BMU)*	76	8023	3927	117,9	20,3	5,8	18	ro(60u)

(ex Panther-97, European Clearway-96)

EUROPEAN PIONEER *(BMU)*	75	14387	7078	140,1	23,4	4,7	18	ro(105u)

(ex Bison-98)

EUROPEAN SEAFARER *(BMU)*	75	10957	4035	141,8	19,4	5,8	18	ro(85u)

(ex Puma-98, Union Trader-80, Union Melbourne-80)

Gateway Investments Ltd

EUROPEAN HIGHLANDER *(BHS)*	78	5897	3046	116,3	18,2	5,4	16	ro(55u)

(ex Lion-98, Merchant Valiant-95, Salahala-90)

P&O NORTH SEA FERRIES LTD.

King George Dock, Hedon Road, Hull, HU9 5QA (01482 795141/fax 01482 706438)
and Ferry Centre, The Dock, Felixstowe, Suffolk, IP11 8TB (01394 604100/fax 01394 604203)

EUROPEAN FREEWAY *(GBR)*	78	21162	6594	184,6	25,3	6,4	17	ro(140u)

(ex Cerdic Ferry-91, Stena Transporter-86, Syria-83, Alpha Enterprise-79)

EUROPEAN TIDEWAY *(GBR)*	77	21162	8672	184,6	25,3	6,4	17	ro(140u)

(ex Doric Ferry-91, Hellas-86, Alpha Progress-79, Stena Runner-77)

Managed and chartered tonnage:

Partenreederei m.s. "Gabriele Wehr"

GABRIELE WEHR *(DEU)*	78	7635	4322	141,3	17,4	5,2	17	ro(70u)

(ex Sari-93, Gabriele Wehr-92, Tor Anglia-85, Gabriele Wehr-82)

Norbank C.V.

NORBANK *(NLD)*	93	17464	6791	166,8	23,9	6,0	23	ro(156u)

Equipment Leasing (Properties) Ltd
NORBAY *(GBR)* 94 17464 6722 166,8 23,9 6,0 23 ro(156u)
Norcape Shipping B.V.
NORCAPE *(NLD)* 79 14087 5024 150,0 20,7 5,1 19 ro(121u)
(ex Tipperary-89, launched as Puma)
B&N Rederi AB
NORCOVE *(SWE)* 77 10279 6671 142,2 19,3 7,0 18 ro(105u)
(ex Cupria-95, Canopus-92, Finnforest-82, Rolita-79)
Oy Rettig Ab
NORKING *(FIN)* 80 17884 11400 170,9 23,0 7,6 19 ro(150u)
(ex Bore King-91)
NORQUEEN *(FIN)* 80 17884 11400 170,9 23,0 7,6 19 ro(150u)
(ex Bore Queen-91)
New building (2)(Aker Finnyards, Rauma) for P&O Charter
NORSKY *(FIN)* 99 11000 179,5 25,2 6,0 20 ro(185u)
NORSTREAM *(FIN)* 99 11000 179,5 25,2 6,0 20 ro(185u)

*The Tees pilot boat passes the **NORQUEEN** at the mouth of the River Tees on 4 August 1998.*
(Dominic McCall)

NatWest Specialist Finance Ltd
PRIDE OF FLANDERS *(GBR)* 78 16776 5455 151,0 23,6 6,5 17 ro(110u)
(ex Nordic Ferry-92, Merzario Hispania-79, Merzario Espania-78)
BMBF (No 15) Ltd
PRIDE OF SUFFOLK *(GBR)* 78 16776 5455 151,0 21,7 6,5 17 ro(110u)
(ex Baltic Ferry-92, Stena Transporter-80, Finnrose-80, Stena Transporter-79)
Partenreederei m.s. "Thomas Wehr"
THOMAS WEHR *(DEU)* 77 7628 4322 141,3 17,4 5,2 17 ro(75u)
(ex Hornlink-94, Fuldatal-94, Santa Maria-93, Mana-93, Thomas Wehr-93, Dana Germania-86,
Tor Neerlandia-85, Thomas Wehr-82, Wacro Express-78, launched as Thomas Wehr)
Tidero A/S
TIDERO STAR *(NIS)* 78 9698 5500 152,3 19,5 6,2 17 ro(90u)
(ex Anzere-91)

P&O SCOTTISH FERRIES LTD.
Jamieson's Quay, PO Box 5, Aberdeen, AB9 8DL (01224 589111/fax 01224 574411)
ST ROGNVALD *(GBR)* 70 5297 3801 103,8 18,8 5,0 16 ro(43u)
(ex Marino Torre-90, Rhone-87, Rhonetal-75, Norcape-74, launched as Rhonetal)

P&O STENA SHIP MANAGEMENT LTD.

Channel House, Channel View Road, Dover, Kent, CT17 9TJ (01304 863000/fax 01304 863223)
Managers for:

Sutten Ltd

EUROPEAN HIGHWAY	(GBR)	92	22986	7550	179,7	28,3	6,3	21	ro(124u)
EUROPEAN PATHWAY	(GBR)	91	22986	7509	179,7	28,3	6,3	21	ro(124u)
EUROPEAN SEAWAY	(GBR)	91	22986	7432	179,7	28,3	6,3	21	ro(124u)

Chartered tonnage:

Stena Ferries Ltd

STENA ROYAL	(BMU)	92	28833	4000	163,4	27,7	6,5	21	ro/px(120u)

(ex Prins Filip-98)

PIKE WARD LTD.

Old Quay, Teignmouth, Devon, TQ14 8EU (01626 772311/fax 01626 770218)
Managers for:

Bartlett Bros (Hauliers) Ltd

TARWAY	(GBR)	58	80	140	25,6	5,2	2,1	7	sd

Note : Laid up Teignmouth and offered for sale.

PRATT ALAN J., ANNETTE, DAVID A., & MICHAEL

770 Lower Rainham Road, Rainham, Gillingham, Kent, ME8 7UB (01634 234147/fax 01634 234147)
Managers for:

Bartlett Creek Shipping Ltd

LOCATOR	(GBR)	70	181	315	31,7	6,8	2,6	7	gen
LODELLA	(GBR)	70	181	315	31,7	6,8	2,6	7	gen
ROAN	(GBR)	61	138	250	27,7	6,5	2,5	7	gen bge
ROGUL	(GBR)	65	172	254	29,4	6,8	2,6	7	gen

Skippered by Captain Peter Herbert, the **ROAN** arrives at Jersey's St Helier Harbour on 2 July 1998 with a cargo of four tons of explosives conveyed in a single container.   (Dave Hocquard

J. J. PRIOR (TRANSPORT) LTD.
Ballast Quay, Fingringhoe, Essex, CO5 7DB (01206 729 412/fax 01206 729 551)

BERT PRIOR *(GBR)*	61	175	289	32,9	6,8	2,5	7	sand
BRENDA PRIOR *(GBR)*	68	198	279	32,3	7,0	2,7	7	sand
(ex Cheryl M-87, Kiption-84)								
J.J. PRIOR *(GBR)* *	15	186	279	33,5	6,5	2,4	7	sand
(ex Peter P-98, Fence-64, X57)								
JAMES PRIOR *(GBR)*	63	191	300	34,1	6,8	2,6	7	sand
(ex James P-95)								
MARK PRIOR *(GBR)*	69	191	295	31,7	6,8	2,6	7	sand
(ex Lobe-94)								
PETER PRIOR *(GBR)*	69	392	609	44,4	7,9	3,2	9	gen
(ex Holm Sound-98, Gore-87, Eloquence-85)								
Chartered Tonnage:								
Alan Jenner								
ROFFEN *(GBR)*	65	172	261	29,4	7,1	2,5	7	sand

*Note : * Laid up Rochester*

NAVIERA QUIMICA S.A.
Edificio Marina Marbella, Avenida Severo Ochoa 28-5°A,, 29600 Marbella, Spain
(+34 902 15 50 00/fax +34 95 276 58 85)
Managers for:

Tanis Ltd								
BENCENO *(IOM)*	77	2612	3971	101,0	14,3	6,4	15	ch tk
Titus Shipping Ltd								
ESTIRENO *(IOM)*	77	2612	3970	101,0	14,3	6,4	15	ch tk
Northern Beta Ltd								
SMERALDO *(IOM)*	98	4896	6713	118,6	16,4	6,5	14	ch tk

THE RAMSEY STEAMSHIP CO LTD.
13 North Quay, Douglas, IoM , IM1 4LE (01624 673557/fax 01624 620460)

BEN ELLAN *(IOM)*	81	538	824	50,0	9,3	3,4	9	gen
(ex River Tamar-90)								
BEN MAYE *(IOM)*	79	548	805	48,8	9,1	3,6	10	gen
(ex Vendome-95, Peroto-94)								
BEN VANE *(IOM)*	77	541	772	50,2	9,0	3,4	9	gen
(ex Bulk Moon-88, Julia S-81)								

*The **BEN VANE** leaves her home port of Ramsey on 27 July 1992.*   *(Danny Kelliher)*

RHEINTAINER LINIE

19 Deichstrasse, Hamburg, Germany (+49 4036 120300)
Chartered tonnage:

Reederei m.s. "Cimbria" Harald Winter KG

RHEIN CARRIER	*(ATG)*	91	3818	4650	103,5	16,2	6,1	14	gen(372c)

(ex Churruca-98, Cimbria-93, Lloyd Iberia-92, Dana Sirena-91, launched as Cimbria)

Harren & Partner Schiffahrts GmbH & Co KG m.s. "Rhein Lagan"

RHEIN MASTER	*(ATG)*	94	3790	4750	100,6	16,5	5,9	15	gen(380c)

(ex Rhein Lagan-96, Paranga-95)

m.s. "Sybille" Reederei Ludtke KG

RHEIN MERCHANT	*(DEU)*	91	3125	4485	89,1	16,2	6,1	14	gen(260c)

(ex Sybille-95, Baltic Bridge-93, Sybille-93)

Heinz Moje KG

RHEIN PARTNER	*(DEU)*	94	3992	5350	101,1	18,4	6,6	15	gen(510c)

(ex Berolin-98, UB Jaguar-97, Iberian Bridge-96, Berolin-94)

Schepers-Rheintrader Schiffahrts KG

RHEIN TRADER	*(DEU)*	91	3815	4155	103,5	16,2	6,1	14	gen(372c)

(ex Rhein Lee-93, Rhein Trader-93)

RIGEL SCHIFFAHRTS GmbH

World Trade Center, Birkenstrasse 15, 28195 Bremen, Germany
(+49 0421 173990/fax +49 0421 1739950)
Managers for:

Rigel Schiffahrts GmbH & Co KG m.t. "Alsterstern"

ALSTERSTERN	*(IOM)*	94	11426	16700	161,4	23,0	8,6	15	oil/ch tk

Rigel Schiffahrts GmbH & Co KG m.t. "Donaustern"

DONAUSTERN	*(IOM)*	95	11426	17078	161,4	23,0	8,6	15	oil/ch tk

Rigel Schiffahrts & Co KG m.t. "Travestern"

HAVELSTERN	*(IOM)*	94	9997	17080	161,4	23,0	8,6	14	oil/ch tk
TRAVESTERN	*(IOM)*	93	9997	17080	161,4	23,0	8,6	15	oil/ch tk

Rigel Schiffahrts GmbH & Co KG m.s. "Isarstern"

ISARSTERN	*(IOM)*	95	11426	17078	161,4	23,0	8,6	14	oil/ch tk

Rigelchem Leda Ltd

LEDASTERN	*(GBR)*	93	6262	10500	123,7	17,7	8,4	12	oil/ch tk

Chemshipping Ltd

ODERSTERN	*(IOM)*	92	5480	9028	109,7	17,7	8,5	12	oil/ch tk

The **ODERSTERN** is about to start loading cargo at Fawley on 14 September 1997.   (Dominic McCall)

Rigel Schiffarhts GmbH & Co KG m.t. "Rheinstern"

RHEINSTERN	*(IOM)*	93	11423	17080	161,4	23,0	8,6	15	oil/ch tk

Chem Carriers Ltd

WESERSTERN	*(IOM)*	92	5480	9028	109,7	17,7	8,5	12	oil/ch tk

ALAN CHARLES RIGGALL

"Dredging" , 11 Penare Road, Penzance, Cornwall, TR18 3AJ
(01736 368614/0831 194086/fax 01736 333080)

SANDCHIME	*(GBR)*	52	190	91	32,0	7,5	2,7	8	grab/suc

Note : Dredging calcified seaweed from Penryn. Also employed on maintenance dredging in UK waters.

J. R. RIX & SONS LTD.

Witham House, 45 Spyvee Street, Hull, HU8 7JR (01482 224422 /fax 01482 210719)
Managers for:

Jemrix Shipping Co Ltd
BREYDON

VENTURE	*(GBR)* *	77	562	1036	45,9	10,0	3,9	9	gen

(ex Wis-86)

*The **BREYDON VENTURE** laid up at Hull on 17 October 1998 shortly before moving down the Humber to Paull for conversion to a tanker.* *(Roy Cressey)*

The Harrix Shipping Co Ltd

HARRIX	*(BHS)*	77	1992	2750	79,1	12,4	5,4	11	gen(104c)

(ex Bettina-98, Barkenkoppel-86, Nordholm-79)

Jonrix Shipping Co Ltd

JONRIX	*(BHS)*	77	1987	2449	79,0	12,5	4,9	11	gen(104c)

(ex Langeland II-94, Langeland-83)

The Lerrix Shipping Co Ltd

LERRIX	*(BHS)*	77	1992	2777	79,1	12,4	5,4	11	gen(104c)

(ex Stefan-98, Sanderskoppel-86)

Lizrix Shipping Co Ltd

LIZRIX	*(BHS)*	77	2019	2899	82,3	13,9	5,3	12	gen(80c)

(ex Yorksee-96, Katharina-90, Karlsvik-86, launched as Eriesee)

Timrix Shipping Co Ltd

TIMRIX	*(BRB)*	77	1973	2224	79,0	12,4	4,8	11	gen(104c)

(ex Kiri-99, Siggen II-97, Siggen-85)

T. & S. Rix Ltd

RIX EAGLE *(GBR)*	90	292	500	50,0	6,0	3,0	8	tk bge
RIX FALCON *(GBR)*	60	172	250	43,3	5,4	2,1	8	tk bge
(ex Burtondale H-92)								
RIX HARRIER *(GBR)*	79	572	1046	45,7	9,5	3,9	9	tk
(ex Breydon Enterprise-96, Wib-87)								
RIX KESTREL *(GBR)*	57	206	320	50,9	5,4	2,3	8	tk bge
(ex Burdale H-93)								
RIX MERLIN *(GBR)*	64	299	520	55,0	6,6	2,5	10	tk bge
(ex Artemisium-96)								
RIX OSPREY *(GBR)*	59	207	300	50,9	5,2	2,3	8	tk bge
(ex Beldale H-96)								

Note : * *Converting to a tanker. To be renamed* RIX HAWK.

RMS (EUROPE) LTD.

Boothferry Terminal, Bridge Street, Goole, DN14 5SS (01405 720707/fax 01405 720740)
Chartered tonnage:
Paul Hase m.s. "Eldor" KG

ELDOR *(DEU)*	81	1441	1795	81,0	11,3	3,3	10	gen(80c)

C. Leyten

VESTING *(NLD)*	92	1587	2166	88,0	11,9	3,6	10	gen

*The **ELDOR** moves slowly up the River Ouse towards Goole on 30 June 1994.* (David H Smith)

ROLF ROHWEDDER REEDEREI

Sonsbecker Strasse 40-44, 46509 Xanten, Germany (+49 02801 71430/fax+49 02801 714315)
Managers for:
Silvaplana Shipping Co (C.I.) Ltd

MEDWAY *(BHS)*	77	1475	2271	69,0	13,5	4,5	9	gen
(ex Sea Medway-94)								

SCOTTISH AGGREGATES LTD.

6 Union Street, Bridge of Allan, Stirlingshire (01786 834055/fax 01786 834381)

TAYSAND *(GBR)*	58	150	280	30,8	6,3	3,0	7	sd
(ex Clyde Enterprise-96)								

SEACON LTD.

Tower Wharf, Northfleet, Kent, DA11 9BD (01474 320 000/fax 01474 329 944)

Chartered tonnage:

Scheepvaartonderneming "Fisker"
SEA CHARENTE *(NLD)*   96   1638   2270   82,5   11,4   3,8   11   gen
(ex Fisker-97)

Briese Schiffahrts GmbH & Co KG m.s. "Elmshorn"
SEA CLYDE *(DEU)*   84   1843   2348   80,1   12,7   4,2   11   gen(102c)
(ex Petena-98)

m.s. "Elbe" Kapitan Bernd Wittkowski KG
SEA ELBE *(ATG)*   86   1636   2271   82,5   11,3   4,2   10   gen(44c)
(ex Silke-95)

Lambertus Switjnk
SEA LOIRE *(NLD)*   91   1272   1685   79,1   10,5   3,7   10   gen
(ex Skylge-97, Terschelling-91)

C.V. Scheepvaartonderneming "Futura"
SEA MAAS *(NLD)*   95   1682   2500   81,7   11,1   4,5   10   gen
(ex Futura-96)

Natissa Shipping Ltd
SEA RHONE *(VCT)*   95   1554   2044   81,6   11,4   3,7   10   gen

C. Vermeulen
SEA RISS *(NLD)*   92   1595   2200   79,7   11,1   4,2   10   gen(164c)
(ex Solon-97)

Rhone Shipping Ltd
SEA RUHR *(VCT)*   95   1554   2044   81,6   11,4   3,7   10   gen

C.V. Scheepvaartonderneming Joriston
SEA SHANNON *(NLD)*   98   1638   2268   82,3   11,4   3,8   10   gen
(launched as Joriston)

m.s. "Neckar" Kapitan Bernd Wittkowski KG
SEA THAMES *(ATG)*   85   1616   2283   82,5   11,4   3,8   10   gen(67c)
(ex Kurt Jensen-94)

Reederei m.s. "Weser" Kapitan Bernd Wittkowski KG
SEA WESER *(ATG)*   86   1616   2283   82,5   11,3   3,8   10   gen(76c)
(ex Jan Meeder-97)

*The **SEA CLYDE** moves into Goole's Ocean Lock on 15 August 1998.*   *(Brian Cook, courtesy ABP Goole)*

SEASCOT SHIPMANAGEMENT LTD.

45 Carrick Street, Glasgow, G2 8PJ (0141 226-3733/fax 0141 204-3276. E-mail: seascot@sol.co.uk)
Managers for:

Seamanx Shipping Ltd

LADY OF CHICHESTER *(GBR)* 70	1056	1726	59,8	12,0	4,4	10	sd
(ex City of Chichester-97, Chichester City-90)

North Bay Shipping Ltd

LESZEK G *(POL)*	77	1991	3285	91,5	13,3	5,1	12	gen(60c)
(ex Leslie Gault-92)

Mukhtar Auezov Ltd

MUKHTAR AUEZOV *(RUS)*	80	4694	5480	124,4	16,4	5,5	13	gen(165c)

Kipsa Co Ltd

PROFESSOR PAPKOVICH *(RUS)*	85	4643	5020	124,2	16,4	5,5	12	gen

SEATRUCK FERRIES LTD.

North Quay, Heysham Harbour, Morecambe, Lancashire LA3 2UL
(01524 853512/fax 01524 853549)

Seatruck Navigation Ltd

MOONDANCE *(BHS)*	78	5881	3046	116,3	18,2	5,4	15	ro(50u)
(ex Merchant Victor-97, Emadala-90)

RIVERDANCE *(BHS)*	77	6041	3046	116,3	18,2	5,4	15	ro(50u)
(ex Sally Eurobridge-96, Eurobridge-94, Sally Eurobridge-94, Schiaffino-93, Tikal-89, Halla-88, Mashala-86)

The company is a wholly owned subsidiary of Crescent Plc

SEAWARD ENGINEERING

974 Pollokshaws Road, Glasgow, G41 2HA (0141 632 4910 /fax 0141 636 1194)

SULBY RIVER *(IOM)*	71	196	269	30,6	7,1	2,4	8	gen
(ex Subro Venture-84)

Note : Laid up repairing at Bowling

SEAWHEEL LTD.

Western House, Hadleigh Road, Ipswich, Suffolk, IP2 0HB (01473 222000/fax 01473 230083)
Chartered tonnage:

CV Scheepvaartonderneming "Heereplein"

HEEREPLEIN *(NLD)*	96	2035	2800	90,0	13,8	4,3	13	gen(205c)

CV Scheepvaartonderneming "Heerestraat"

HEERESTRAAT *(NLD)*	97	2035	2850	90,1	13,9	4,3	13	gen(205c)

Partenreederei m.s. "John Bluhm"

CHRISTINE O *(DEU)*	78	1925	2262	79,8	12,8	4,4	12	gen(145c)
(ex John Bluhm-98)

m.s. "Linda Buck" Schiffahrts KG

LINDA BUCK *(ATG)*	85	2295	2584	95,9	14,2	4,1	10	ro(180c)
(ex Britannia-96, RMS Britannia-93, Linda Buck-93)

m.s. "Rolf Buck" Schiffahrts KG

ROLF BUCK *(ATG)*	85	2295	2591	95,9	14,2	4,1	10	ro(180c)

Operated by Rheintainer Ltd:

Pride of Braila B.V.

PRIDE OF BRAILA *(NLD)*	98	2077	3200	110,0	11.4	3.6	13	cc(190c)

Pride of Veere B.V.

PRIDE OF VEERE *(NLD)*	98	2034	3200	110,0	11,4	3,6	13	cc(190c)

See also ARKLOW SHIPPING *for other chartered tonnage.*

*Seawheel's **HEEREPLEIN** heads up the River Ouse towards Goole on 19 April 1997 with a good load of containers.* *(David H Smith)*

SEVERN SANDS LTD.
14 Westgate Chambers, Commercial Street, Newport, Gwent (01633 220842/fax 01633 253976)
Managers for:
    Crossavon Ltd

SEVERN SANDS *(GBR)*	60	515	676	51,7	9,2	3,7	9	sd

    (ex Ferlas-95, Le Ferlas-89, Isca-77)

SHELL U. K. OIL LTD.
Room 789, Shell-Mex House, Strand, PO Box 148, London, WC2R 0ZA
(0171 257-3000/fax 0171 257-3440)
Managers for:
    Shell U.K. Ltd

ACHATINA *(GBR)*	68	1580	2654	84,3	12,5	4,7	14	tk

    (ex Shell Craftsman-93, Ardrossan-79)

AMORIA *(GBR)*	81	1926	3027	79,3	13,2	5,5	12	tk

    (ex Shell Marketer-93)

ARIANTA *(GBR)* .	82	1926	3027	79,3	13,2	5,5	12	tk

    (ex Shell Technician-93)

ASPRELLA *(GBR)*	81	1926	3027	79,2	13,2	5,5	12	tk

    (ex Shell Seafarer-93)
Time chartered tonnage:
    Troms Fylkes Dampskibsselskap A/S

BJARKØY *(NOR)*	97	1637	2490	85,3	12,1	5,1	12	tk

SILVER LINE LTD.
Gate House, 1 Farringdon Street, London EC4M 7NS (0171 489-0088/ fax 0171 489-0529)
Commercial managers for:
    Halifax Shipping Ltd

CHELTENHAM *(BHS)*	90	3376	4318	99,6	15,8	5,8	13	lpg

    Diamond Bridge Shipping Co Ltd

COTSWOLD *(PAN)*	89	3368	4143	99,1	15,8	5,7	13	lpg

    (ex Diamante-91, Pennine-91)

Euromarine Inc.

EVERDINA *(PAN)*	81	2698	3043	93,4	14,4	5,3	13	lpg

MC Pelerin Shipping Ltd

MALVERN *(BHS)*	90	3368	4148	99,1	15,8	5,7	13	lpg

Almak Shipping Ltd

SILVER DREAM *(PAN)*	97	4402	3800	99,0	18,2	5,1	14	lpg

MC Osprey Shipping Ltd

SNOWDON *(BHS)*	89	3219	3814	99,1	16,0	5,4	13	lpg

SLOMAN NEPTUN SCHIFFAHRTS - AKTIENGESELLSCHAFT

PO Box 101469, 28014 Bremen, Germany (+49 421 1763-314/fax+49 0421 1763-300)
Managers for:

Deltagas Shipping Co Ltd

DELTAGAS *(LBR)*	92	3011	3700	88,4	14,2	6,2	14	lpg

Gammagas Shipping Co Ltd

GAMMAGAS *(LBR)*	92	3703	4447	99,4	15,0	6,5	15	lpg

SOENDERBORG REDERIAKTIESELSKAB (SONDERBORG STEAMSHIP CO. LTD.)

Havnevej 18, PO Box 20, 6320 Egernsund, Denmark (+45 74 441435/fax +45 74 441475)
Managers for:

Clovis Navigation S.A.
GERARD PATRICK

PURCELL *(PAN)*	70	2978	2568	88,5	13,9	5,5	13	l/v

(ex Deichtor-83, Lubbecke-83, Ibesca Belgica-80, Ibesca Britannia-78, Lubbecke-77)

K/S Philomena

PHILOMENA PURCELL *(DIS)* 73		3013	2650	88,3	13,0	5,0	13	l/v

(ex Esteflut-82)

SOUTH COAST SHIPPING CO. LTD.

Baltic Wharf, Elm Street, Marine Parade, Southampton, SO1 4 5JF
(01703 720200/fax 01703 334528)

SAND FALCON *(GBR)*	98	5307	9128	99,9	19,5	7,9	12	sd
SAND FULMAR *(GBR)*	98	5307	9128	99,9	19,5	7,9	12	sd
SAND HARRIER *(GBR)*	90	3751	5916	99,0	16,5	6,6	11	sd
SAND HERON *(GBR)*	90	3751	5916	99,0	16,5	6,4	11	sd
SAND KESTREL *(GBR)*	74	3110	4722	98,7	18,2	5,1	13	sd
(ex Bowherald-94)								
SAND KITE *(GBR)*	74	3110	4425	98,7	18,2	5,1	13	sd
(ex Bowknight-93)								
SAND SERIN *(GBR)*	74	1283	2120	66,6	12,2	4,8	10	sd
SAND SWAN *(GBR)*	70	1204	1944	66,6	12,5	4,4	10	sd
SAND WEAVER *(GBR)*	75	3497	5271	96,4	16,7	6,1	12	sd

Managers for:

RMC Aggregates (South Wales) Ltd

BOWCROSS *(GBR)*	67	1006	1786	59,8	12,0	4,3	10	sd
(ex Chichester Cross-71)								
WELSH PIPER *(GBR)*	87	1251	1923	69,0	12,5	4,4	11	sd

SOUTH WEST WATER PLC.

Peninsula House, Rydon Lane, Exeter, Devon, EX2 7HR (01392 219666/fax 01392 444694)

COUNTESS WEAR *(GBR)*	63	237	366	37,5	7,5	3,1	8	sludge

(ex S.W.2-75)

ST HELIER PORT SERVICES LTD.
New North Quay, St Helier, Jersey, Channel Islands, (01534 870300/fax 01534 830234)
Managers for:
Aggregate Industries UK Ltd

RONEZ *(GBR)*	82	870	1117	64,7	10,1	3,5	10	ce

STANDARD MARINE SERVICES LTD.
4th Floor, Mountbatten House, Grovesnor Square, Southampton, SO15 2UX
(01703 821200/fax 01703 821390)
Managers for:
Esso Marine UK Ltd

PETRO AVON *(GBR)*	81	2386	3122	91,3	13,1	5,6	12	oil/bit tk
(ex Esso Avon-94)								
PETRO MERSEY *(GBR)*	72	11898	20510	166,5	22,8	9,2	15	tk
(ex Esso Mersey-94)								
PETRO SEVERN *(GBR)*	75	11897	20087	166,5	22,9	9,2	15	tk
(ex Esso Severn-94)								
PETRO TYNE *(GBR)*	74	13340	22333	161,2	23,6	9,8	13	tk
(ex Esso Tyne-94, Esso Saint Petersburg-90, Esso Callunda-85)								

STENA LINE LTD.
3rd Floor, East Wing, Charter House, Park Street, Ashford, Kent, TN24 8EX
(01233 647022/fax 01233 202391)
Managers for:
P&O Stena Line Ltd

STENA CALEDONIA *(GBR)*	81	12619	2206	129,7	21,6	4,8	19	ro/px(62u)*
(ex St David-91)								
STENA CHALLENGER *(GBR)*	91	18523	4650	157,3	24,3	5,5	17	ro/px(120u)*
STENA GALLOWAY *(GBR)*	80	12175	1895	129,4	21,6	4,7	18	ro/px(62u)*
(ex Galloway Princess-91)								
STENA SEARIDER *(GBR)*	69	20914	14800	178,7	24,5	5,7	18	ro(150u)
(ex Norse Mersey-95, Stena Searider-92, Searider-92, Stena Searider-91, Scandinavia Link-90, Scandinavia-87, Polaris-84, Finncarrier-75)								

Lily Shipping B.V.

STENA SEATRADER *(NLD)*	73	17991	6850	182,7	22,1	6,2	17	ro(130u)
(ex Svea Link-90, Svealand av Malmo-87, Svealand-82)								

Chartered tonnage operated by Stena Freight, Harwich
m.s. "Apus" Rohden Schiffahrts GmbH & Co KG

APUS *(DEU)*	90	2606	3100	90,0	13,0	4,6	12	gen(198c)
(ex Anke Ehler-98)								

Uwe von Allworden KG m.s. "Hera"

HERA *(DEU)*	90	2660	3240	90,0	13,0	4,6	11	gen(198c)

*Note : * trading freight only   See also* NORTHERN MARINE MANAGEMENT

AB STENA MARINE
Danmarksterminalen, Masthuggetskajen, 40519 Gothenburg, Sweden
(+46 031 858000/fax +46 031 120651)
Managers for:
Stena Carrier Ltd

STENA CARRIER *(CYM)*	78	13117	8661	151,0	20,5	7,3	16	ro(562c)
(ex Jolly Smeraldo-83, Jolly Bruno-82, Stena Carrier-82, Imparca Miami-81, Stena Carrier-80, Imparca Express I-80)								

STEPHENSON CLARKE SHIPPING LTD.

Eldon Court, Percy Street, Newcastle upon Tyne, NE99 1TD (0191 232-2184/fax 0191 261-1156)

Name		Year							Type
BIRLING	(IOM)	77	2795	4300	91,3	14,6	5,4	14	gen
DALLINGTON	(GBR)	75	7788	12140	137,6	18,7	7,9	14	gen
DONNINGTON	(GBR)	75	7788	12134	137,6	18,7	7,9	14	gen
DURRINGTON	(IOM)	81	7788	11990	137,6	18,7	7,9	14	gen
EMERALD	(IOM)	78	2795	4300	91,3	14,6	5,5	14	gen
HARTING	(IOM)	81	2813	4300	91,3	14,6	5,8	12	gen(32c)
SEA AMETHYST	(IOM)	87	8254	11901	142,9	20,1	7,2	12	bulk
(ex Amethyst-97, Cardona-93)									
STEYNING	(IOM)	83	2808	4300	91,3	14,6	5,8	12	gen(32c)
STORRINGTON	(IOM)	82	7788	11990	137,6	18,7	7,9	14	gen

Commercial managers for:

Assiduous AS

Name		Year							Type
ARENDAL BAY	(NIS)	74	7482	11848	135,7	19,3	8,3	12	bulk
(ex Gem-98, Guardo-92)									

Civil & Marine Ltd

Name		Year							Type
CAMBROOK	(BHS)	82	2318	3020	99,8	11,4	4,3	10	gen
(ex Lena Wessels-87)									

Joint Lease Ltd

Name		Year							Type
JEVINGTON	(IOM)	77	7702	12328	127,4	19,5	8,1	13	bulk
(ex Elizabete-89, Garrison Point-88)									

Container Finance Ltd

Name		Year							Type
NORTHUMBRIAN WATER	(GBR)	77	1068	1654	72,5	14,6	3,4	12	sludge

Time chartered tonnage:

Aldrington KS

Name		Year							Type
ALDRINGTON	(BHS)	78	4297	6570	103,6	16,1	7,0	14	gen

Ashington KS

Name		Year							Type
ASHINGTON	(BHS)	79	4297	6570	103,6	16,1	7,0	14	gen

Scheepvaart Bedrijf Tendo

Name		Year							Type
TENDO	(NLD)	95	2050	3370	88,0	12,8	4,9	13	gen(115c)

Stephenson Clarke Shipping Ltd demise chartered to **Losinjska Plovibda Brodarstvo,** Mali Losinj

Name		Year							Type
WASHINGTON	(HRV)	77	6400	9008	127,0	18,7	7,6	14	gen

The **STEYNING** loads stone at Llysfaen Jetty, Llanddulas, on 30 March 1997.   (John P Evans)

STEWART CHARTERING LTD.

Meridian House, Royal Hill, Greenwich, London, SE10 8RW (0181 853 4646/fax 0181 853 5459)
Commercial managers for:

Ionian Island Corp.

ATHINOULA *(VCT)*	72	1454	2489	77,2	13,0	4,7	13	gen

(ex Eurolord-95, Maemi-92, Cederborg-85, Carebeka VII-83, Nortrio-74)

Major Marine Enterprises S.A.

GALCREST *(PAN)*	83	2638	4129	84,7	14,5	6,2	11	gen

(ex Aki Ace-97, Kumiko L-91, Sun Rose-88, Seizan-86)

Medfee Shipping Ltd

PAUL *(VCT)*	74	1427	1853	77,9	11,5	4,9	12	gen

(ex Rapla-96)
Chartered tonnage:

Rederij Marathon

MARATHON *(ANT)*	76	1655	2575	78,7	12,4	5,0	11	gen

(ex Vrouwe Alida-90)

Southern Marine Services N.V.

MARINER *(ANT)*	66	1148	1821	73,0	12,1	5,0	11	gen

(ex Armada Mariner-83, Dicky-79, Kraftca-75)

Rederij Kwekkeboom

VOYAGER *(NLD)*	75	1746	2790	78,4	12,4	5,4	12	gen

(ex Baron-96, Barok-95, Audrey Johanna-81)

*The **PAUL** at anchor off the Spanish port of Tarragona on 8 June 1997.* (Barry Standerline)

STOLT-NIELSEN SHIPPING LTD.

Aldwych House, 71-91 Aldwych, London, WC2B 4HN (0171 404 4455/fax 0171 831 3100)
Commercial operators for:

Stolt-Nielsen Northern Services Corp.

STOLT AVOCET *(CYM)*	92	3853	5749	99,9	16,8	6,8	12	ch tk
STOLT DIPPER *(CYM)*	91	3206	4759	96,4	15,3	6,2	13	ch tk

(ex Margit Terkol-96, Stolt Margit Terkol-94)

STOLT GUILLEMOT *(CYM)*	93	3204	4676	96,4	15,3	6,2	13	ch tk

(ex Sasi Terkol-96)

STOLT KESTREL *(CYM)*	92	3853	5742	99,9	17,1	6,8	12	ch tk
STOLT PETREL *(CYM)*	92	3206	4761	96,4	15,3	6,2	13	ch tk

(ex Edny Terkol-96)

STOLT TERN *(CYM)*	92	3206	4759	96,4	15,3	6,2	13	ch tk

(ex Jytte Terkol-96, Stolt Jytte Terkol-92)

Stolt Shipholding (Gibraltar) Ltd

STOLT KITE *(CYM)*	92	3204	4710	96,4	15,3	6,2	13	ch tk
(ex Randi Terkol-96)								
STOLT KITTIWAKE *(CYM)*	93	3204	4710	96,4	15,3	6,2	13	ch tk
(ex Astrid Terkol-96)								
STOLT SHEARWATER *(CYM)*	98	3550	5498	96,2	16,4	6,6	12	ch tk
New buildings (2) (Inma, Italy) - option further 3								
STOLT CORMORANT *(CYM)*	early 99	3550	5498	96,2	16,4	6,6	12	ch tk
STOLT FULMAR *(CYM)*	late 99	3550	5498	96,2	16,4	6,6	12	ch tk

SWIFT NAVIGATION CO. LTD.
c/o Regal Agencies Corp., 145 Filonos Street, 185 36 Piraeus, Greece.
(+30 453.7138/fax +30 451.2842)

GEEST ATLAS *(BMU)*	96	2906	3950	99,5	16,4	5,0	15	cc(340c)
(ex Bell Atlas-97)								

TOR LINE AB
Tor Line Terminal, Skandiahnen PO Box 8888, 402 72 Gothenburg, Sweden.
(+ 46 31 65 09 33/fax + 46 31 65 08 90)

TOR GOTHIA *(GBR)*	71	12259	7385	163,5	21,0	7,1	16	ro(100u)
TOR HOLLANDIA *(GBR)*	73	12254	7362	163,5	21,1	7,2	16	ro(100u)
(ex Tor Dan-93, Tor Dania-92, Bandar Abbas Express-78, Tor Dania-75)								

TORBULK LTD.
The Old Rectory, Bargate, Grimsby, Nth Lincolnshire, DN34 4SY (01472 242363/fax 01472 242329)
Fosseway Shipping Ltd

FOSSELAND *(BHS)*	79	1059	1559	66,9	10,8	4,1	11	gen(58c)
(ex Perelle-94)								

Managers for:
Estuary Shipping Ltd

SEA HUMBER *(BHS)*	77	1602	2139	69,0	13,5	4,5	10	gen

Swanland Shipping Ltd

SEA TRENT *(BRB)*	77	1475	2273	69,0	13,5	4,5	9	gen
(ex Sea Avon-96)								

Cove Shipping Co Ltd

SWANLAND *(BRB)*	77	1978	3150	81,0	13,9	5,4	12	gen
(ex Elsborg-96, Artemis-94, Elsborg-88, Carebeka IX-83)								

See also Onesimus Dorey (Shipowners) Ltd *under* F. T. EVERARD

The **SEA HUMBER** off the Hook of Holland on 21 May 1997. *(Jan van der Klooster)*

TRANSEUROPA SHIPPING LINES

Ferry Terminal, Ramsgate New Port, Ramsgate, Kent, CT11 (01843 585151/fax 01843 853992))
Chartered tonnage:

EUROVOYAGER *(CYP)*		78	6612	1992	118,4	20,7	4,5	22	ro/px(55u)
(ex Prins Albert-98)									
Baron Shipping Co Ltd									
JUNIPER *(CYP)*		77	5610	2700	109,7	17,5	5,2	16	ro(36u)
(ex Cap Benat-86)									

*The **JUNIPER** was photographed at Rosslare on 5 July 1994.* (Vic Smith)

TRANSMARINE MANAGEMENT ApS

1st Floor, Holbergsgade 26, 1057 Copenhagen, Denmark (+45 33 93 25 25/fax +45 33 93 89 81)
Managers for:

Prime Commercial Investment Ltd									
AMARANT *(IOM)*		69	1726	2545	86,4	12,0	5,2	12	ch tk
(ex Kimia Maju-86, Chemical Sprinter-84)									
AMETIST *(IOM)*		93	2728	4572	94,5	15,0	6,1	15	ch tk
(ex Hang Chang No.8-96)									
Amber Shipping Ltd									
AMBER *(IOM)*		97	2893	4999	99,9	15,4	6,3	12	ch tk
(ex Fortune Athena-98)									

TYNE WATER BOATS LTD.

9 King George Road, South Shields, Tyne & Wear, NE34 0SP
(0191 427 0991 & 0860 899928/ fax 0191 425 2340)

ABERCRAIG *(GBR)*	*	45	138	180	31,7	6,0	2,2	8	wt tk bge
(ex Ernie Spearing-74, Attunity-67, VWL 12-52, MOB 9-46)									
HARCUSS *(GBR)*		32	96	150	26,5	5,2	2,7	8	wt tk bge
Note : * Laid up Tyne									

UNIFLEET B.V.

PO Box 314, 4700 AH Roosendaal, Netherlands (+ 31 165 578444/ fax + 31 165 571444)
Managers for:

Emilia Shipping Ltd

EMILIA THERESA *(IOM)*	98	3356	5250	103,5	16,0	5,8	12	ch tk

UNION TRANSPORT GROUP PLC.

Imperial House, 21-25 North Street, Bromley, Kent, BR1 1SJ (0181 290-1234/fax 0181 289-1592)

UNION ARBO *(BHS)*	84	1522	1899	82,5	11,4	3,5	10	gen(80c)
(ex Birka-94)								
UNION JUPITER *(BRB)*	90	2230	3274	99,7	12,6	4,3	11	gen(114c)
UNION MARS *(BRB)*	81	986	1448	69,9	11,3	3,4	11	gen
UNION PEARL *(BRB)*	90	2230	3274	99,7	13,0	4,3	11	gen(114c)
(ex Bromley Pearl-95)								
UNION PLUTO *(BRB)*	84	1521	1762	82,5	11,4	3,5	10	gen(80c)
(ex Phönix 1-95, Phoenix-94, Osterburg-87)								
UNION TITAN *(BRB)*	86	1543	2376	87,7	11,1	3,9	10	gen(98c)
UNION TOPAZ *(BRB)*	85	1543	2362	87,7	11,1	3,9	10	gen(98c)
(ex Bromley Topaz-92, Union Topaz-90)								
UNION VENUS *(BRB)*	84	1522	1899	82,5	11,4	3,5	10	gen(48c)
(ex Pinguin-95, Hansa-89)								

Managers for:

Rederij H. Steenstra

DOUWE S *(NLD)*	87	1311	1771	79,7	11,3	3,7	10	gen(78c)
(ex Torpe-94)								
UNION-ELISABETH *(NLD)*	97	1905	2655	88,6	12,6	4,0	10	gen

Rederij P. Doorenweerd

UNION ROBIN *(NLD)*	83	1501	2310	78,6	12,1	4,2	10	gen
(ex Elisabeth S-95)								

Chartered tonnage:

Bridgetown Shipping KS

UNION MOON *(BRB)*	85	1543	2362	87,7	11,1	3,9	10	gen(98c)
UNION NEPTUNE *(BRB)*	85	1543	2376	87,7	11,1	3,9	10	gen(98c)
UNION SUN *(BRB)*	85	1543	2376	87,7	11,1	3,9	10	gen(98c)

*Now the smallest vessel in the Union Transport fleet, the **UNION MARS** heads down the River Medway from Rochester on 16 April 1998.*
(Peter Hutchison)

UNITED EUROPEAN CAR CARRIERS (NORWAY) A.S. (UECC)

PO Box 265, 4891 Grimstad, Norway (+ 47 37 04 90 00/fax +47 37 04 45 63)

Newbuildings (2) (Tsuneishi)	00			140,0	22,7		22	vc(1400a)

Managers for:

United European Car Carriers (IOM) Ltd

AUTOCARRIER (NIS)	82	6421	1472	89,5	18,3	4,3	13	vc(662a)
(ex Castorp-90)								
AUTOFREIGHTER (NIS)	77	5927	1313	89,3	18,3	4,2	13	vc(750a)
(ex Fredenhagen-90)								
AUTOLINE (NIS)	83	7069	1550	100,0	17,0	4,8	12	vc(650a)
AUTOPREMIER (NIS)	97	11591	4443	126,9	20,0	6,2	20	vc(1150a)
AUTOPRIDE (NIS)	97	11591	4442	126,9	20,0	6,2	20	vc(1150a)
AUTOROUTE (NIS)	79	7114	1894	100,0	17,4	4,2	15	vc(670a)
AUTOTRANSPORTER (NIS)	83	7069	1566	100,0	17,0	4,8	12	vc(650a)
DONINGTON (NIS)	76	5351	1400	105,5	15,9	4,2	15	vc(634a)
(ex Tertre Rouge-87)								
INDIANAPOLIS (NIS)	80	4743	1956	88,8	17,4	4,8	14	vc(1460a)
JARAMA (NIS)	80	4743	1956	88,8	17,4	4,8	14	vc(650a)

United European Car Carriers (UK) Ltd

AUTOPROGRESS (NIS)	98	11591	4442	126,9	20,0	6,2	20	vc(1150a)
Newbuilding (Frisian Ship)	May 99	11591	4442	126,9	20,0	6,2	20	vc(1150a)

The **AUTOPREMIER** leaves Southampton on 28 May 1997.   (Chris Bancroft)

THE UNITED KINGDOM GOVERNMENT (Dept of Environment for Northern Ireland)

1 College Square East, Belfast, BT1 6DR

DIVIS II (GBR)	79	802	892	56,0	11,2	3,3	10	sludge

UNITED MARINE DREDGING LTD. (UMD)

Francis House, Shopwyke Road, Chichester, West Sussex, PO20 6AD

(01243 780082/fax 01243 782873)

CITY OF CARDIFF (GBR)	97	2074	2845	72,0	15,0	5,2	11	sd
CITY OF CHICHESTER (GBR)	97	2074	2845	72,0	15,0	5,2	11	sd

Managers for:
U.M.D. City of London Ltd

CITY OF LONDON *(GBR)*	89	3660	5989	99,8	17,5	6,3	12	sd

U.M.D. City of Westminster Ltd

CITY OF WESTMINSTER *(GBR)*	90	3914	6604	99,9	17,7	6,7	12	sd

V SHIPS (UK) LTD.
Enterprise House, Ocean Way, Ocean Village, Southampton, SO14 3XB
(01703 634477/fax 01703 634319)
Managers for:
Cenargo International Ltd

BRAVE MERCHANT	98	19710	6300	180,0	25,0	6,5	24	ro/px(146u)
DAWN MERCHANT	98	19710	6300	180,0	25,0	6,5	24	ro/px(146u)
New buildings (2) (Astilleros)								
	Jun	99						
	Nov	99						

See also BELFAST FREIGHT FERRIES and MERCHANT FERRIES

THOMAS WATSON (SHIPPING) LTD.
252 High Street, Rochester, Kent, ME1 1HZ (01634 844632/4/fax 01634 831838)
Managers for:
Andrean Shipping Ltd

LADY ELSIE *(CYP)*	75	1031	1593	65,8	10,7	4,3	10	gen
(ex Canvey-92, Velox-88)								
LADY REA *(CYP)*	78	1954	3265	81,7	14,1	5,5	12	gen
(ex Ortrud-90, Carib Sun-88, Reggeland-87, Sylvia Delta-85)								

Veneto Shipping Co Ltd

LADY SERENA *(CYP)*	95	2394	3697	87,4	12,3	5,4	11	gen(144c)
(ex Espero-96)								

Downlands Shipping Inc

LADY SOPHIA *(BHS)*	77	2208	4083	82,1	13,3	6,6	10	gen(32c)
(ex Enns-95, Norned Thor-84, Holberg-79, Atlantic Progress-77)								

Lakehead Shipping Ltd

LADY SYLVIA *(BHS)*	79	1707	2701	73,4	13,2	5,1	11	gen
(ex Inishfree—94, Arklow Vale-88, Capricorn-85)								

The **LADY SYLVIA** makes stately progress in the Bristol Channel on 2 April 1998.   *(Danny Lynch)*

ANDREW WEIR SHIPPING LTD. (AWS)
Dexter House, 2 Royal Mint Court, London, EC3N 4XX (0171 265-0808/fax 0171 816-4992)

BALTIC EAGLE *(IOM)*	79	14738	9450	137,1	26,0	8,2	18	ro(354c)
BALTIC EIDER *(IOM)*	89	20865	13866	157,7	25,3	8,5	19	ro(700c)
BALTIC TERN *(IOM)*	89	3896	3754	106,6	16,2	5,4	13	cc(316c)
CITY OF MANCHESTER *(IOM)* 79		3992	4352	104,2	16,8	5,7	14	cc(300c)

(ex Laxfoss-85, City of Hartlepool-84)

PACHECO *(IOM)*	78	3992	4352	104,2	16,8	5,7	14	cc(300c)

(ex City of Lisbon-98, Cervantes-96, City of Plymouth-93)

Chartered tonnage:

Reederei m.s. "Regia" Heinz Freese KG

CERVANTES *(ATG)*	94	5026	6449	117,0	- 18,1	6,9	16	cc(538c)

(ex Regia-97, Portland Bay-96, Regia-94)

Corona Schiffahrtsges mbH & Co KG

CITY OF DUBLIN *(CYP)*	78	17414	25329	166,1	28,6	11,6	18	cc(1282c)

(ex City of Antwerp-98, City of London-97, Pacific Span-93, Incotrans Pacific-90, ScanDutch Arcadia-90, Korean Senator-88, Corona-87, Atlantic Corona-85, ScanDutch Corona-84, launched as Corona)

Linaria Maritime Inc.

CITY OF GLASGOW *(GRC)*	78	14050	15270	157,1	25,1	9,2	18	cc(956c)

(ex Express-98, Choyang Express-98, Express-93, MSC Laura-90, Zim Guam-90, Express-88, Durga Osaka-87, Express-87, Nedlloyd Express-86, TFL Express-86, Alltrans Express-80)

Schiffahrtsges "Hansa Hamburg" mbH & Co

CITY OF ISTANBUL *(ATG)*	92	9600	12583	149,5	22,6	8,3	18	cc(1012c)

(ex Saudi Buraydah-98, Maersk Bogota-94, launched as Major)

KG m.s. "Northern Harmony" Schiffhrtsgesellschaft mbH & Co.

CITY OF TUNIS *(ATG)*	94	19819	20252	174,5	27,4	9,4	19	cc(1709c)

(ex Northern Harmony-94)

Kapitan Manfred Draxl Schiffsbetriebs GmbH & Co KG m.s. "Gudrun"

PELAYO *(ATG)*	95	4628	5660	113,1	16,4	6,1	16	cc(510c)

(ex City of Oporto-98, Jane-98, Gudrun-95)

WESSEX SHIPPING LTD.
111 Victoria Street, Bristol (0117 929 0620/fax 0117 929 2774)

Time chartered tonnage:

Papilla Shipping Co Ltd

POETENITZ *(CYP)*	82	1934	2890	88,0	11,5	4,7	11	gen(90c)

(ex Diogo do Couto-95, Svenja-86)

WEST OF SCOTLAND WATER
Shieldhall Sewerage Treatment Works, 38 Renfrew Road, Glasgow, G51 4SU
(0141 842-5847/fax 0141 842-5850)

DALMARNOCK *(GBR)*	70	2182	3266	95,4	15,6	4,4	12	sludge
GARROCH HEAD *(GBR)*	77	2702	3671	98,7	16,0	4,4	11	sludge

Note: Laid up Clyde pending sale.

THE WHITAKER GROUP
Crown Dry Dock, Tower Street, Hull, HU9 1TY (01482 320444/fax 01482 226270) John H. Whitaker (Tankers) Ltd - Southern Division - Ocean Road Eastern Docks, Southampton, SO1 1AH (01703 339989/fax 01703 339925) and John Harker Ltd - Runcorn Office (0192 85 75001)

WHITCREST *(GBR)*	70	2144	3430	91,3	13,1	5,9	14	tk

(ex Esso Tenby-94)

John H. Whitaker (Tankers) Ltd - Humber Area

FARNDALE (GBR) *	67	293	500	55,4	5,7	2,8	8	tk bge
(ex Farndale H-89)								
FOSSDALE H (GBR) *	67	293	500	55,4	5,7	2,4	8	tk bge
FUSEDALE H (GBR) *	68	293	500	55,4	5,7	2,4	8	tk bge
HUMBER ENDEAVOUR (GBR)	81	380	650	60,8	6,0	2,4	8	tk bge
(ex Fleet Endeavour-92)								
HUMBER ENERGY (GBR) +*	83	380	650	60,8	6,0	2,4	8	tk bge
HUMBER ENTERPRISE(GBR) *	67	295	450	55,4	5,7	2,4	8	tk bge
HUMBER FUELLER (GBR) +*	57	192	300	43,8	5,5	2,4	7	tk bge
HUMBER JUBILEE (GBR)	77	382	650	60,9	6,0	2,7	9	tk bge
HUMBER PRIDE (GBR)	79	380	650	60,8	6,0	2,4	8	tk bge
HUMBER PRINCESS (GBR) +*	79	380	650	60,8	6,0	2,4	8	tk bge
HUMBER PROGRESS (GBR)	80	380	650	60,8	6,0	2,4	8	tk bge
HUMBER STAR (GBR) *	69	274	400	45,7	6,6	2,2	7	tk bge
(ex Wade Stone-77)								

Note : * Laid up Goole. +* Laid up Hull .

John Harker Ltd - Mersey Area

DEEPDALE H (GBR)	65	385	580	46,2	8,3	3,4	7	tk bge
(ex Riverbeacon-67)								
DOVEDALE H (GBR) ++	62	306	550	47,5	6,6	2,7	7	tk bge
(ex Riverbridge-67)								
WHARFDALE H (GBR)	60	609	1126	61,9	8,8	3,2	8	tk bge
(ex Olympic 1-81, Esso V-80)								
WHITKIRK (GBR)	69	730	1219	64,6	9,2	3,7	10	tk
(ex Borman-89)								

Note : ++ Laid up Runcorn.

John H. Whitaker (Tankers) Ltd - Milford Haven Area

WHITHAVEN (GBR)	72	1204	1933	66,2	11,5	5,0	11	bk tk
(ex Frank C-94, Shell Director-93, Caernarvon-79)								
WHITSEA (GBR)	71	728	1229	64,3	9,3	3,7	10	tk
(ex Bude-92)								
WHITANK (GBR) *	76	686	1030	61,0	9,3	3,7	11	tk
(ex Luban-87)								
WHITIDE (GBR)	70	1148	2083	74,5	10,2	4,9	11	tk
(ex Lindvag-90, Tarnvik-78)								

Note : * Laid up Truro.

The **WHITANK** lies in Hull's fish dock on 8 January 1995. (Richard McCart, courtesy ABP Hull)

John H. Whitaker (Tankers) Ltd - Southampton Area

BATTLESTONE *(GBR)*	68	293	500	55,4	5,7	2,4	9	tk bge
(ex Battlestone C- 89, Battle Stone-76)								
BORROWDALE H *(GBR)* **	72	385	550	50,6	6,7	3,1	8	tk bge
JAYNEE W *(GBR)*	96	1689	2901	75,3	12,8	5,2	10	bk tk
TEESDALE H *(GBR)*	76	499	1050	43,9	10,0	3,9	8	tk
(ex Wilks-86)								
WHITASK *(GBR)*	78	640	844	57,3	10,9	2,9	10	tk
(ex Bromley-93)								

Managers for;

Twinpeek Shipping Co Ltd

WHITMARINER *(CYP)*	78	1363	2562	88,8	11,4	4,4	12	tk
(ex Pallieter-98, Pierre Lafitte-90)								

Note : ** Laid up Southampton pending sale.

John H. Whitaker (Tankers) Ltd - Thames/Dover

WHITSPRAY *(GBR)*	69	899	1321	64,6	11,1	3,4	10	tk
(ex Bristolian-93)								
WHITSTAR *(GBR)*	68	999	2140	74,3	10,2	4,8	11	bk tk
(ex Furena-91, Furenas-90, Stardex-79, Lone Wonsild)								

Note. See also R. LAPTHORN *and* FALMOUTH OIL SERVICES

WILLIAMS SHIPPING MARINE LTD.

Berth 21, Ocean Road, Eastern Docks, Southampton, SO14 3GF
(01703 237330/fax 01703 236151)

MURIUS *(GBR)*	62	125	213	29,8	6,2	2,0	7	gen bge

CHARLES M. WILLIE & CO. (SHIPPING) LTD.

Celtic House, Britannia Road, Roath Basin, Cardiff, CF1 5LS (01222 471000/fax 01222 471999)

BEGONA B *(ESP)*	92	3779	5861	92,8	17,1	6,6	13	gen(300c)
(ex Nenufar Uno, Celtic Crusader-96, Euro Trader-95, Celtic Crusader-93)								
CELTIC COMMANDER *(BHS)*	93	3840	5833	92,8	17,2	6,5	13	gen(361c)
(ex Fairway-96, Celtic Commander-94)								
CELTIC ENDEAVOUR *(BHS)*	88	2034	3366	85,1	13,0	6,0	11	gen
(ex Iberian Sea-98, launched as Ahmet Madenci II)								
CELTIC NAVIGATOR *(BHS)*	79	1010	1538	65,8	11,1	4,3	10	gen
(ex Wilant-89, Marant-88, Engel Klein-83)								
LOUISE BORCHARD *(BHS)* *	97	3840	6250	100,0	17,0	6,4	15	gen(467c)
(ex Celtic Princess-97)								

*The **CELTIC ENDEAVOUR** was photographed in the Bristol Channel on 13 July 1998.*   *(Danny Lynch)*

Managers for:

Charles M. Willie Co (Investments) Ltd

CELTIC AMBASSADOR *(BHS)* 94	3739	5788	92,8	17,2	6,5	13	gen(381c)
(ex Fairwind-96, Celtic Ambassador-94)							
EMILY BORCHARD *(BHS)* * 97	4015	6250	101,0	17,0	6,4	15	gen(467c)
(ex Gracechurch Meteor-97, launched as Celtic Monarch)							
JUDITH BORCHARD *(BHS)* * 95	4015	6250	100,0	17,0	6,4	15	gen(467c)
(ex Gracechurch Sun-97, Celtic Prince-96)							
RUTH BORCHARD *(BHS)* * 96	4015	6250	100,8	17,2	6,4	15	gen(467c)
(ex Gracechurch Comet-97, Celtic Sovereign-96)							

Newbuilding (Madenci,Karadeniz):

CELTIC KING *(BHS)* 99	4015	6250	101,0	17,0	6,4	15	gen(467c)

Time chartered tonnage:

Baltway Shipping Ltd

CELTIC VENTURE *(BHS)* 71	1285	1533	79,0	11,1	4,1	12	gen(77c)
(ex Norman Commodore-91)							
CELTIC VOYAGER *(BHS)* 75	1015	1519	65,7	10,8	4,1	10	gen
(ex Alannah Weston-84)							
IBERIAN COAST *(BHS)* 79	1029	1391	72,2	11,3	3,3	11	gen
(ex Yulence-87, London Miller-81)							
IBERIAN OCEAN *(BHS)* 79	1029	1391	72,2	11,3	3,3	11	gen
(ex Zealence-87, Birkenhead Miller-82)							

Note : * Chartered to BORCHARD LINES LTD qv

WILSON SHIP MANAGEMENT (BERGEN) AS

PO Box 4145, Sandbrugaten 5, Dreggen, 5023 Bergen, Norway
(+47 55 31 03 20/fax +47 55 31 37 66)
Managers for:

S.D. Shipping Ltd

KARI ARNHILD *(PAN)* 94	9855	16073	148,0	20,5	5,3	14	bulk

WORLDFAST SHIPPING LTD.

Unit 1, Orwell House, Ferry Lane, Felixstowe, Suffolk, IP11 8QL (01394 676032/fax 01394 607451)
Agents only for the following operating on KNSM (P&O Nedlloyd) charter:

Partenreederei Jorg Kopping m.s. "Hamburg"

HAMBURG *(DEU)* 91	3466	4610	96,7	15,8	6,0	14	gen(343c)
(ex Judith Borchard-97, Hamburg-91)							

Partenreederei m.s. "Rendsburg"

RENDSBURG *(ATG)* 91	3469	4610	96,7	15,8	6,0	14	gen(343c)
(ex Ruth Borchard-97, Rendsburg-91)							

Owners/managers of the following vessels have not been fully identified

CARMEL *(HND)* 71	199	411	41,8	7,7	2,7	9	gen
(ex Valour-93, Subro Valour-91, Ferryhill II-78)							

Detained by MCA in Grimsby

EILIDH OF KISHORN 60	93	120	24,5	5,0	1,5	8	gen bge
(ex Needles-82)							

Operating West Coast of Ireland (fish farm)

HELGAFELL *(IOM)* 94	6297	7968	121,9	20,3	7,6	16	gen(703c)
(ex Heidi B-97, Maersk Euro Quonto-97, launched as Heidi B)							

Abbreviations for vessel types

asp tk	asphalt tanker
bk tk	oil bunkering tanker
bk tk bge	oil bunkering tank barge
bulk	bulk carrier
cc(c)	container carrier (container capacity in Twenty foot Equivalent Units [TEUs])
cem	bulk cement carrier
ch tk	chemical tanker
drg/hpr	suction dredger/hopper
ed oil tk	edible oil tanker
ed oil bge	edible oil tank barge
eff tk	effluent tanker
eff tk bge	effluent tank barge
fish	vivier tank fish carrier
gen	general cargo
gen(c)	general cargo (container capacity in TEUs)
gen bge	general cargo barge
gen bge(cr)	general cargo barge fitted with crane
gen/pt	general cargo/palletised cargo
gen/ro	general cargo/RoRo facility on deck
gen/ro/ch	general cargo/RoRo facility on deck/chemicals in wing tanks
gen(sl)	general cargo/slurry
grab/suc	grab/suction dredger
lpg	liquified gas tanker
lpg(ch)	liquified gas tanker - chlorine
l/v	livestock carrier
nuc	spent nuclear fuel carrier
oil/bit tk	oil/bitumen tanker
oil/ch/bit tk	oil/chemical/bitumen tanker
oil/ch tk	oil/chemical tanker
oil/veg tk	oil/vegetable oil tanker
ref	refrigerated cargo
ro(u)	RoRo cargo (capacity in 13,6m trailer units)
ro(u/a)	RoRo cargo (capacity in 13,6m trailer units/automobiles)
ro h/l	RoRo heavy lift cargo
ro/pt	RoRo pallet carrier
ro/px(u)	RoRo passenger (capacity in 13,6 m trailer units)
sand	sand and aggregate carrier
sd	sand/aggregate suction dredger
sludge	sludge carrier
tk	oil tanker
tk bge	oil tank barge
tk bge/gen	tank barge/general cargo
vc(a)	vehicle carrier (car capacity)
wt tk bge	potable water tank barge

Key to Flags

(ANT)	Netherlands Antilles
(ATF)	Kerguelen Islands
(ATG)	Antigua & Barbuda
(BHS)	Bahamas
(BLZ)	Belize
(BMU)	Bermuda
(BRB)	Barbados
(CYM)	Cayman Islands
(CYP)	Cyprus
(DEU)	Germany
(DIS)	Denmark (Danish International Register)
(ESP)	Spain
(EST)	Estonia
(FIN)	Finland
(GBR)	United Kingdom)
(GIB)	Gibraltar
(HND)	Honduras
(HRV)	Croatia
(IOM)	Isle of Man
(IRL)	Irish Republic
(ITA)	Italy
(KHM)	Croatia
(LBR)	Liberia
(MLT)	Malta
(NIS)	Norway (Norwegian International Register)
(NOR)	Norway
(NLD)	Netherlands
(PAN)	Panama
(POL)	Poland
(ROM)	Romania
(RUS)	Russia
(VCT)	St Vincent & the Grenadines

The **SOLWAY FISHER** approaches Greenock at the end of a voyage from Glensanda with a cargo of stone on 9 August 1996.
(John Lucas)

SHIP NAME INDEX

Current names are in capital letters. All previous names of vessels are listed in lower case letters.
* = launched as   ** = completed as

BRAVE MERCHANT	66	
BREAKSEA	17	
Bregenz	31	
BRENDA PRIOR	51	
Brendonia	29	
BRENDONIAN	29	
BRENTWOOD	17	
Bressay Sound	4	
Brevik	45	
Breydon Enterprise	54	
BREYDON VENTURE	53	
BRIARTHORN	27	
Bridgeman *	27	
Bristolian	69	
Britannia	56	
BRITANNIA BEAVER	12	
BRITISH SHIELD	11	
BRITISH TAMAR	11	
Bromley	69	
Bromley Pearl	64	
Bromley Topaz	64	
Bruarfoss	22	
BRUCE STONE	16	
Bude	68	
Buffalo	48	
Bulk Moon	51	
BUNA	4	
Burdale H	54	
BURE	17	
BURHOU I	4	
Burtondale H	54	
Busby	16	
BUSTARDTHORPE	15	
Busy Bee	31	
BUSY GRACE	31	
Cableman	28	
Cadence	17	
Caernarvon	68	
Caledonian	32	
Cambeck	7	
Cambourne	7	
CAMBRAE	7	
CAMBROOK	60	
Camdijk	7	
CAMIRA	20	
Canaima	24	
CANDOURITY	24	
Candy	45	
Candy I	45	
Canopus (2862/79)	28	
Canopus (10279/77)	49	
CANOPUS 1	29	
Canvey	66	
CAP AFRIQUE	25	
Cap Benat	63	
Capacity	24	
Cape Spirit	3	
Capricorn	66	
CAPTION	14	
Caravelle	12	
Cardona	60	
Carebeka VII	61	
Carebeka IX	62	
Cari-Star	15	
Carib Sun	66	
Caribbean Sky	48	
Caribbean Stream	46	
Carina	6	
CARMEL	70	
CAROLE T	13	
Carrick Kestrel	46	
Castorp	65	
Catarina	13	
Catarina Caldas	13	

Catherine Schiffino	25	
CECIL GILDERS	43	
Cederborg	61	
CELEBRITY	44	
Celestine **	22	
Celia	26	
CELTIC 4	12	
Celtic Crusader	69	
Celtic Monarch*	70	
Celtic Prince	70	
Celtic Princess	69	
Celtic Sovereign	70	
CELTIC TERRIER	13	
CELTIC X.....	69, 70	
Cerdic Ferry	48	
CERVANTES	67	
Cervantes	67	
Charcrest	16	
Charles Trigon	20	
CHARLOTTE	34	
CHARLOTTE BORCHARD	11	
Charmo	45	
CHARTSMAN	28	
Chemical Sprinter	63	
CHELTENHAM	57	
Chemist Lisbon *	43	
CHERYL C	13	
Cheryl M	51	
CHESHAM	33	
Chichester City	56	
Chichester Cross	58	
Choyang Express	67	
CHRISTIAN	24	
Christian	23	
CHRISTINE O	56	
Christopher Caribe	15	
CHRISTOPHER MEEDER	15	
Churruca	52	
Cimbria	52	
City of Antwerp	67	
CITY OF BARCELONA	18	
City of Chichester	56	
CITY OF DUBLIN	67	
CITY OF GLASGOW	67	
City of Hartlepool	67	
CITY OF ISTANBUL	67	
City of Lisbon	67	
City of London	67	
CITY OF MANCHESTER	67	
City of Manchester	25	
City of Oporto	67	
City of Plymouth	67	
CITY OF SUNDERLAND	18	
CITY OF TUNIS	67	
CITY OF X.....	65, 66	
CLARA	33	
Clarknes	14	
Claudia W	43	
CLEMENTINE	22	
Clyde Enterprise	54	
CMBT Cutter	10	
COASTAL X.....	15	
COEDMOR	19	
Comity	31	
COMMODITY	44	
COMMODORE X.....	15	
Concordia	31	
CONFORMITY	24	
CONNEMARA	20	
CONOCOAST	5	
Conostream	5	
CONSORTIUM 1	46	
CONTENDER	47	
CONTRACTOR	5	
Contractor	32	

Contship Two	16	
CONVEYOR	5	
Cormorant	37	
CORNET	12	
CORONA	28	
Corona	67	
Cortia	26	
Cortina	45	
COTINGA	23	
COTSWOLD	57	
COUNTESS WEAR	58	
Cowdray	5	
Cowes	29	
Craigallian	27	
Craigantlet	15	
Craigavad	15	
Craigmore	43	
CREAR	29	
CRESCENCE	17	
CRISTALLO	26	
Crown Link *	3	
Cupria	49	
CUXHAVEN	10	
CYMBELINE	21	
DALHEM	16	
DALLINGTON	60	
DALMARNOCK	67	
Dana Germania	49	
DANA HAFNIA	22	
Dana Sirena	52	
Daniel	6	
Daniel D	6	
Daniella	6	
DART 4	9	
DART X.....	17, 18	
Daunt Rock	12	
David Dorman	4	
David M	28	
David Marley	10	
David W	29	
DAWN MERCHANT	66	
DEEPDALE H	68	
Deepstone	7	
Deer Sound	4	
Deerhurst	30	
Deichtor	58	
DELSTOR	5	
DELTAGAS	58	
DENHAM	33	
Diamante	57	
Dicky	61	
DICTION	16	
Dintel	43	
Diogo do Couto	67	
DIVIS II	65	
Dommel	43	
DONALD REDFORD	46	
DONAUSTERN	52	
DONINGTON	65	
DONNINGTON	60	
Doric Ferry	48	
DOROTHEA SCHULTE	19	
Dorte	20	
Dorthe Boye	9	
DOUGLAS McWILLIAM	18	
DOUWE S	64	
DOVEDALE H	68	
DOWLAIS	13	
Dublin	11	
Duino	22	
Duke of Anglia	38	
Duke of Flanders	45	
DUNANY	5	
DUNKERQUE EXPRESS	8	

Merchant Valiant	48	
Merchant Victor	56	
MERCHANT X.....	43	
Mercurius	6	
Merino *	31	
MERLE	9	
MERSEY FISHER	28	
MERSEY VIKING	45	
Merzario Arabia	22	
Merzario Espania	49	
Merzario		
Hispania (15525/78)	26	
Merzario		
Hispania (16776/78)	49	
Merzario Ionia	26	
Merzario Persia	22	
Michael Ane	46	
Michael M	28	
MILFORD FISHER	27	
MILLAC STAR II	12	
MINKA C	13	
MOB 9	63	
Mobil Lubchem	11	
Moidart	44	
Moon Trader	37	
MOONDANCE	56	
MSC Laura	67	
MUKHTAR AUEZOV	56	
Multitank Antares	43	
Murell	4	
MURIUS	69	
Natalie	23	
Nathum	43	
Navajo	28	
Nedlloyd Express	67	
Needles	70	
Needwood	10	
Nenufar Uno	69	
Neptun	4	
Neptunus	15	
Nestor	46	
Nestor 1	46	
Neukloster	31	
Neuwerk	31	
NEW GENERATION	26	
Newfyne	4	
N.F. Jaguar	34	
NICKY L	36	
Nicole	13	
Niekerk	9	
Niewiadow	5	
Nopal Norte	30	
NOR.....	48, 49	
Norbrit Hope	13	
Norbrit Rijn	13	
Norcape	49	
NORCLIFF	3	
Nord Skagerrak *	3	
NORD STAR	44	
Nordholm	53	
Nordic Ferry	49	
Nordicus One	26	
Nordlicht II	47	
NORDSTRAND	13	
Norgas Mariner	30	
Norgas Transporter	30	
NORLEADER	46	
Norman Commodore	70	
NORMANTON	38	
Normed Thor	66	
NORSE MERSEY	48	
Norse Mersey	59	
Norsea	48	
Norsklint	6	
Norsky	48	
NORSTAR	43	
NORSTONE	46	
NORTH SEA TRADER	23	
Northern Harmony	67	
NORTHERN STAR	14	
NORTHGATE	28	
Northsea Trader	31	
NORTHUMBRIAN WATER	60	
Nortrio	61	
Norwegian Challenger	43	
Norwegian Crusader	43	
Oahu	33	
OAK	6	
OARSMAN	28	
Ocean Hunter	32	
OCTOGON 3	19	
ODERSTERN	52	
Oiltrans 31	12	
Olympic 1	68	
Onabi	32	
ONWARD MARINER	5	
Ordinence	44	
ORTAC	4	
Ortrud	66	
Ortrud Müller	37	
Oscona	11	
Osterburg	64	
OTTO BECKER	45	
Oyster Bay	48	
PACHECO	67	
Pacific Span	67	
Pagai	33	
Pallieter	69	
PAMELA EVERARD	23	
Panarea 1	33	
PANARY	29	
Panther	48	
PANURGIC	37	
Paranga	52	
Partnership	20	
Patmarie	46	
PAUL	61	
PAVO	25	
Peacock Venture	37	
PELAYO	67	
Pellworm	15	
Penda	34	
Pennine	57	
PENTLAND	24	
Pentland	11	
Pentland Moor	30	
Per	17	
Perelle	62	
PERFECTO	45	
Peroto	51	
Perseus	18	
Persia	22	
Petena	55	
Peter P	51	
PETER PRIOR	51	
PETRO X.....	59	
Petuja *	11	
PEVERIL	34	
PHILOMENA PURCELL	58	
Phoenix	64	
Phönix 1	64	
PICASSO	24	
Pico Ruivo	47	
Pierre Lafitte	69	
Pinewood	27	
Pinguin	64	
PLANET V	20	
Platessa	24	
POETENITZ	67	
Poker	24	
Polaris	59	
Polo III	36	
Portland	31	
Portland Bay	67	
PRIDE OF BRAILA	56	
PRIDE OF VEERE	56	
PRIDE OF X.....	49	
Primo	15	
PRIMROSE	18	
Princesse Marie Christine	18	
Prins Albert	63	
Prins Filip	50	
Procyon	27	
PROFESSOR		
PAPKOVICH	56	
Puma (10957/75)	48	
Puma * (14087/79)	49	
PUR	47	
PURBECK	14	
Quarterman *	27	
QUENTIN	30	
Quimico Leixoes	43	
Quimico Lisboa	43	
RACHEL BORCHARD	11	
RAIDER	26	
Ran *	5	
Randi Terkol	62	
Rapid	12	
Rapla	61	
Raute	28	
REBECCA HAMMANN	37	
REDTHORN	27	
Regent Wren	32	
Reggeland	66	
Regia	67	
Reina del Cantabrico	18	
RENDSBURG	70	
RH 13	31	
Rhein Carrier	15	
Rhein Feeder	15	
Rhein Lagan (3818/91)	10	
Rhein Lagan (3790/94)	52	
Rhein Lee (2463/91)	15	
Rhein Lee (3815/91)	52	
Rhein Liffey	10	
RHEIN X.....	52	
RHEINSTERN	53	
Rhombus	28	
Rhone	49	
Rhonetal	49	
Richard	28	
RISBY	18	
Ritzberg*	19	
RIVER DART	30	
RIVER LUNE	9	
River Tamar	51	
Riverbeacon	68	
Riverbridge	68	
RIVERDANCE	56	
RIX X.....	54	
RMS Anglia	37	
RMS Bavaria	36	
RMS Britannia	56	
RMS Hollandia	34	
RMS Scotia	37	
ROAN	50	
ROBETA	21	
Rockabill (3329/84)	25	

TAYSAND	54	Tuzla	45	VWL 12	63
Teal 1	4	Tweed	34	Wachau	28
TED GRACE	30	TYNE FISHER	28	Wacro Express	49
TEES FISHER	28	UB Jaguar	52	Wade Stone	68
TEESDALE H	69	Ulster Industry	25	Wakefield	16
TENDO	60	Underas Sandtag VI	6	WALTER HAMMANN	36
TERRY GRACE	30	UNDINE	22	Wargon IV	19
Terschelling	55	Unicorn Michael	32	WASHINGTON	60
Tertre Rouge	65	UNIKA	33	WEAR FISHER	28
Texel Bay	31	Union Melbourne	48	WELSH PIPER	58
TFL Express	67	Union Mercury **	13	WESER	20
THALIA	3	Union Saturn *	13	WESERSTERN	53
THAMES FISHER	28	Union Sun	46	West Moor	6
THAMES RAPID	12	Union Topaz	64	Westermoor	6
The Dutch	36	Union Trader	48	WESTERN TRADER	26
THOMAS WEHR	49	UNION-ELISABETH	64	WESTGATE	28
Thunar	44	UNION X.....	64	WHARFDALE H	68
Thuntank 2	28	United Terrier	13	WHEATCROFT	32
TIDERO STAR	49	Uranus	31	Wheelsman *	27
Tikal	56	URGENCE	17	WHIT.....	67 - 69
TILLERMAN	28	UTE	33	WHITONIA	25
Tina Saturn	13			Whitonia	35
Timmerland	26	Val Metavro *	3	Wib	54
TIMRIX	53	Vallmo	22	WIGHTSTONE	46
TINA C	14	Valour	70	WIKNER	32
TINNES	15	Vanda	14	Wilant	69
Tipperary	49	Vanessa	13	WILBERNIA	29
Tommelise	32	VANESSA C	13	Wilhelmina V	6
TOMMY	16	VARBOLA	18	WILHELMINE STEFFENS	37
Topaz	21	Vasaland	26	Wilks	69
Torpe	64	VECTIS FALCON	14	Willonia	23
Tor Anglia	48	VECTIS ISLE	13	Wis	53
Tor Dan	62	Vega	22	Wotan	34
Tor Dania	62	Velox	66	Wuppertal	24
Tor Neerlandia	49	Vendome	51	Wycliffe	30
TOR X.....	62	Venern *	45	X 57	51
TORDUCT	16	Ventura	6		
Torfen	5	Verena	27	YARROW	30
TORKSEY	38	VESTING	54	YEOMAN ROSE	15
TORRENT	38	Viaduct	16	Yorksee	53
TRACY BENNETT	12	VIBRENCE	17	Yulence	70
Transgermania	10	VIC 47	19	YVETTE	20
TRAQUAIR	30	VIC 72	18		
TRAVESTERN	52	Victory	13	Zealence	70
Trinity Bay	32	Viking Trader	48	Zeeland	10
Trojborg	24	Visbur	32	Zim Australia	31
Trude	6	VITA	44	ZIM ESPANA	6
TURBULENCE	17	VOYAGER	61	Zim Guam	67
Tutova	19	Vrouwe Alida	61		

*The **TEESDALE H** was photographed at Poole in July 1997.*   (Krispen Atkinson)

The suction dredger **ARCO HUMBER** has been laid up on the River Tees since 1990. She was photographed on 10 November 1998.   (Michael Green)

F T Everard's **SPECIALITY** arrives at Belfast with a full cargo of timber on 30 May 1995.

(Alan Geddes)